S0-AQH-227

8/86

TWO DOZEN RED ROSES

TWO DOZEN RED ROSES

BY

ROSEMARY HAMMOND

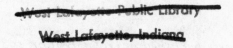
MILLS & BOON LIMITED
15–16 BROOK'S MEWS
LONDON W1A 1DR

8/86 Thorndike 10.40

First published in Great Britain 1984
by Mills & Boon Limited

© Rosemary Hammond 1984

Australian copyright 1984
Reprinted 1984
Large Print edition 1986

ISBN 0 263 11108 3

Set in Monophoto Plantin 16 on 18½ pt.
16–0386 – 46587

Made and printed in Great Britain by
Richard Clay (The Chaucer Press) Ltd,
Bungay, Suffolk

CHAPTER ONE

'Is the lion in his den?'

Warren Langley leaned over Sarah's neat desk and inclined his blond head briefly towards the closed door at his right. Voices could be heard from within.

Sarah allowed herself a fleeting smile. She made it a firm practice never to discuss her boss or his cases with anyone, not even the young lawyers in the firm. She decided to make an exception with Warren because in the year he had been working there, fresh out of law school, he had rapidly become Sloan Sheridan's right-hand man.

'It's the new client. Dr Alvarez.' Sarah riffled through the pages of a notebook, half filled with shorthand symbols. 'You know how he is with them.'

Warren rolled his blue eyes heavenward.

'Don't I ever! And not just with clients, either, I might add.'

Sarah shrugged. 'It's part of his battle plan. He lets them know right off the bat who's boss, and they always end up trusting him. It seems to work.'

Warren gave her a dubious look. 'Yes, but does he have to be quite so—so—forceful?'

'Apparently so,' she replied drily. She adjusted her glasses, clear glass with no correction, and turned back to her typewriter.

Still Warren lingered, idly toying with the stapler on her desk. 'How long have you worked for Sloan?' he asked.

Sarah paused in the midst of inserting a fresh piece of paper in her typewriter and thought a moment, calculating. The sun coming in through the window glinted on her honey-coloured hair, smooth and heavy, combed severely back from her forehead and caught in a loose bun at the nape of her neck.

'Let's see, it will be five years in January.'

'Do you like working for him?'

Sarah turned her greenish hazel eyes on him in a cool stare, suddenly wary. She worked hard to create a detached, impersonal image in the office, and Warren's question came a little too near the personal to suit her. She saw him flinch and back off a little at her dismissing glance and softened her expression.

'Why the inquisition?' she asked lightly. Fledgling lawyers were tender plants with fragile egos. Warren was still in that tentative stage of his career where he was so unsure of himself and his abilities that any criticism at all distressed him.

Sarah wondered if her boss had ever gone through that painful stage. Somehow she didn't think so. It was hard to imagine Sloan Sheridan ever abashed by anything, from wild animals with bared teeth to royalty, much less a mere secretary.

She knew, however, that their close working relationship and the hard-earned trust Sloan had finally placed in her gave her a certain cachet, a position of some importance in the firm, and that some of the awed reverence other lawyers had for her boss spilled over on to her.

'Well, do you?' Warren persisted.

'Like working for him? Yes, very much.'

She didn't elaborate. She had learned that involved explanations only led to mis-understandings, and she was almost par-anoid about discussing her boss or her job. How could she explain, without gushing sentimentality, that working for Sloan Sheridan, one of San Francisco's most prominent and successful trial lawyers, gave such a vividness to her life, that it had become the focal point of her existence?

'I thought so,' Warren went on. 'I don't blame you.' He frowned. 'It's funny, though.'

'What's funny?' She wished he would go. She had to get the Alvarez notes typed up before the end of the day, and she knew that after the noisy interview still going on in the adjacent office, Sloan would have more dictation for her.

'You like working for Sloan,' Warren went on, 'that's obvious. But I get the impression you dislike him. As a person, that is.'

Sarah masked her startled reaction to Warren's comment with a cold stare.

'You're quite mistaken,' she said curtly. 'I have no feelings about him one way or the other.'

She turned back to her work, angry with herself for having said too much. That was what she got, she thought, for feeling sorry for young lawyers! In future, she'd be more careful.

After all, Warren Langley was not so young. She knew from her personnel file that he was twenty-eight, two years older than she was, and older than most new graduates. He had been a late starter.

'Hey, I'm sorry,' he was saying now in a worried voice. 'No offence meant. It's none of my business.'

In control of herself once again, she allowed him a distant, cool smile. 'It's all right, Warren,' she said calmly. 'I just don't believe in mixing business with my personal life.'

There, I've said too much again, she thought, and fought down a feeling of annoyance at Warren. It wasn't his fault. She'd been subjected to similar inquisitions in the past. Everyone seemed to be curious about the remote Sarah Kincaid and her relations with the volatile Sloan Sheridan. With practice she had learned to parry personal questions with an offhand remark, a dismissive gesture. She must be tired.

At that moment the door to Sloan's office burst open. A tall dark man appeared at the door and immediately Sarah's small office seemed to be filled with his presence. He seemed to have that effect wherever he was, whether in the office, in a restaurant or in a courtroom.

Sloan Sheridan was a presence. His dark brown eyes, almost black, seemed to be everywhere, seeing into corners lesser mortals overlooked. His lean, tautly muscled frame gave an unforgettable impression of barely-leashed power, and the dark face with its high-bridged, imperious nose looked upon the world as an Indian warrior astride a white charger might, faintly contemptuous, condescending, and totally in control of himself and any situation that might arise.

His dark eyes flicked to the stocky fair man still hovering over Sarah's desk, and Sarah suppressed a smile at the look of sheer terror that had flickered momentarily in Warren's face at Sloan's sudden appearance.

'Haven't you got anything better to do, Langley, than bother my secretary? She's got work to do.'

Warren mumbled something incoherent about needing to clarify something on a point of law.

'Go research it yourself,' Sloan snapped. 'That's what you're paid for.' He turned to Sarah. 'Kincaid, have you got those Alvarez notes typed up yet?'

Sarah reached for the stack of typewritten pages on her desk as Warren slunk as unobtrusively as possible out the door, and handed them to Sloan.

'I'm not quite through,' she said calmly, 'but I think this is the substance of it.'

He took the papers from her and glanced quickly through them. 'I need the rest by noon, so get cracking!'

'Yes, Mr Sheridan,' she murmured inaudibly as she turned the page of her notebook.

'What was that remark?' His voice was ominous.

Sarah raised her eyes slowly to his, her face a pleasant but impersonal mask.

'I said, "Yes, Mr Sheridan",' she repeated in a clear voice.

He grunted then and went back into his own office, shutting the door firmly behind him. Immediately, Sarah's own office seemed empty, peaceful, serene, as though a dangerous animal had decided not to eat its helpless victims this time after all.

She sighed and began mechanically to type up her remaining notes. With part of her mind she thought about Warren's remark. Did she like Sloan Sheridan? She had never really given the matter much thought. It was like asking if she 'liked' a prowling panther in the jungle or a marauding pirate. He was simply a force of nature. One admired him for his powers, but he was not a man who invited personal affection.

As his secretary, Sarah served him well, catered to his sometimes unreasonable demands, soothed his occasional black rages, and supported him in his work so efficiently and unobtrusively that she knew she had become very valuable to him, if not indispensable.

No human being would ever be indispensable to Sloan Sheridan, she thought, recalling the steady stream of beautiful women he had been involved with during the years she had worked for him. In spite of his Olympian attitude towards the world, he was, after all, a man, with a man's needs.

And, she added wryly to herself with a

little smile, there seemed to be an abundance
of women eager and willing to fill whatever
those needs might be. Sarah had had to cope
with a few of them herself, and had not
enjoyed the experience. She shuddered
when she thought of the scenes she had
overheard coming from that private office,
the telephone conversations, the brutal
rejections, the tears.

No, she decided, I don't like him. This
admission surprised her a little, because he
certainly was an intensely attractive man.
He was always impeccably dressed in ultra-
conservative dark suits, immaculate white
shirts and muted ties, as though the ferocity
of his true nature was somehow masked,
made to appear more civilised through this
subdued exterior.

His thick straight hair, black and coarse,
flecked here and there with strands of grey,
was always cut to perfection and combed
neatly. Yes, she thought again, a decidedly
attractive man.

She noticed, then, that she had typed the

same sentence three times. Dismissing thoughts of Sloan Sheridan firmly from her mind, she ripped out the ruined page, tore it in several pieces and threw it in the wastebasket. As she put a clean sheet into the typewriter, she promised herself that she would not allow herself to speculate about him as a man ever again. Such thoughts interfered with her powers of concentration, and inefficiency was simply not tolerated by her formidable boss. He'd fire her in a minute, she knew, if it became a habit.

That afternoon, Sloan called her into his office, as she had anticipated, to dictate the notes of his meeting that morning with his new client, Dr Alvarez.

It looked to be an interesting case, she thought now as she settled herself in the chair across from Sloan's wide desk. But then, all his cases were interesting. It was one reason she enjoyed working for him. He only took the cases that interested him and was offered far more than he could handle.

She watched him now as he leafed

through the terse notes he had made during the morning's interview with the client. She recognised those strong black strokes of the pen covering several pages and gave a little sigh. It would be a long afternoon. Half a page of his concise notes meant at least a whole typewritten page, single-spaced.

'Am I boring you, Mrs Kincaid?' The dark eyes snapped up at her from the page.

'Not at all, Mr Sheridan,' she replied evenly.

She gave him a cool look. He grunted and returned to his notes. Sarah watched him, fascinated as always by the total concentration he gave his work. The minutes ticked by. She glanced briefly out of the window, her mind and ears still alert for the first sign that he was ready for her.

It was a grey windy day in early December. Soon it would be Christmas again, she thought, and made a mental note to herself to get at her gift list tonight. Her sister and her family would be coming up from Santa Barbara. It would be nice to see her small nephew again.

She heard the rustle of paper, the slight squeak of the swivel chair as he changed his position that meant Sloan had organised his thoughts and was ready to dictate. She turned back to him.

He was still deep in thought, his lips pursed, his eyes hooded. As she watched, she saw him lift a large strong hand to rub the back of his neck and thought he looked tired. She noticed, too, how his thick eyelashes lightly brushed the high planes of his prominent cheekbones.

He really was a striking-looking man, she thought, not classically handsome, but with rugged good looks that made for a powerful, unforgettable impression.

Suddenly his eyes flicked up and fastened on her, surprising the look of appraisal on her face. Damn Warren Langley and his probing questions, she thought, knowing she blushed and, worse, knowing Sloan was aware of it.

He raised his heavy dark eyebrows in a questioning look, the dark eyes faintly mocking. Then he straightened up in his chair.

'Ready, Kincaid?'

She nodded, pen poised, and he began to dictate.

He was a superb dictator, the low voice clearly understandable, his thoughts so well organised that there was never a boring lull while he collected them, yet never so fast that she had to strain to keep up with him. She knew, however, that she had to give him all her attention. One phrase missed, and she'd be lost.

It was a fascinating case. Dr Alvarez was a middle-aged, highly-respected physician, a paediatrician, whose thriving practice was in Marin County, just across the Golden Gate Bridge. He had been accused by a fourteen-year-old patient and her mother of taking indecent liberties with the girl in the course of an examination. Such an accusation, if proved, would be the ruin of any doctor, but especially one entrusted with the care of young girls.

As Sloan dictated, she instinctively began to visualise the line his defence of the doctor would take. Somehow he must prove to a jury that the girl had not only invited the doctor's attentions, but that he had rejected them and that she had then accused him out of pique.

It was a slim chance, she thought, as her pen raced across the page to keep up with him, but if anyone could pull it off, Sloan could. It would depend on what the girl was like. And her mother. He seemed to be focusing his attention on the mother, and Sarah wondered what he was leading up to.

She was so absorbed in keeping up with Sloan's steady dictation and her own speculations about the case that she didn't realise someone else had appeared at the open door of the office until she heard a light tapping on it.

She looked up to see a very beautiful dark-haired woman lounging against the

doorframe. She was swathed in a gorgeous mink coat with a matching hat tilted at a rakish angle. One hand rested on a curved hip, pulling the fur aside to reveal a stunning figure in a red wool dress.

The woman's dark flashing eyes were fastened greedily on the man behind the desk, the red lips curled in a provocative smile.

'I hope I'm not interrupting anything, darling.' The voice was low, throaty, seductive, but Sarah, recovered by now from her surprise, thought she detected a note of uncertainty in it. Sheleaned back a little in her chair, watching and waiting.

At the first sound of the woman's voice, Sloan's head had turned swiftly, and there was no mistaking the anger in those dark eyes. Sarah had seen that look too often to leave her in any doubt that her boss was furious at the interruption.

'Leonie—what are you doing here?' The voice was cold and cut through the silence like a knife.

The woman's expression faltered at his tone, but she quickly recovered her composure and took a step towards the man at the desk.

'We have a dinner date,' she reminded him lightly. 'Don't tell me you've forgotten!'

'I haven't forgotten.' His tone was icy. 'That doesn't answer my question. What are you doing here?'

Sarah saw him lean back slightly in his chair, the tension leaving his face. Disgust and scathing contempt were etched on every plane and angle, and she suddenly felt sorry for Leonie. It was almost preferable to feel the sting of his wrath, she thought, than to find oneself the victim of that cold rejection.

'But it's almost five o'clock,' Leonie said.

Sarah winced at the pleading note in her voice. There was going to be a scene. Her one thought now was to get out of there as unobtrusively as possible. Let him handle his own discarded women, she thought resentfully. In another minute Leonie would be in tears, and after her gruelling day, Sarah was in no mood to pick up the pieces.

As if he had read her mind, Sloan turned his attention to her.

'That will be all, Kincaid,' he said. 'Type up what you've done tonight. I'll need the notes for a meeting at eight o'clock tomorrow morning.'

Sarah was tempted to throw her notebook across the desk at him, but she knew where that would lead in his present mood. She'd just have to stay and do it. She rose from her chair.

'Yes, Mr Sheridan,' she said through clenched teeth, glaring down at him.

He gave her a look, then, an eyebrow raised, a mocking glint in his eyes, and she thought she could detect a faint smile flicker briefly on his set mouth.

She lifted her head high and walked towards the door to her own office, passing close to the now-trembling Leonie as she did so, and catching a whiff of a cloying perfume.

She saw, too, the look Leonie gave her, appraising the tailored black suit, the neat white blouse, the severe hairstyle, glasses and absence of make-up. Perversely, the look of dismissal in the other woman's over-bright eyes annoyed her. Even though Sarah went to great lengths to preserve a colourless, even dowdy, appearance, no woman likes to be looked at by another as a harmless, inoffensive part of the background.

'Excuse me,' Sarah murmured as she brushed by her.

She went into her office, closing the connecting door firmly behind her. Immediately, voices were raised, one shrill, verging on hysteria, the other a low, firm monotone.

'You know my rule about coming to the office, Leonie,' came Sloan's hard relentless voice.

Sarah set her jaw and closed her ears. 'Damn him,' she said aloud as she settled herself at her typewriter. 'He knows it's past quitting time and I want to go home.'

She attacked the keys, and the clatter drowned out the sounds of battle coming from within Sloan's office. She typed steadily for perhaps half an hour. Everyone else had gone home. She would have to take a later train.

It was dark outside by now and had started to rain. She hadn't brought either a raincoat or umbrella and she knew she would get soaked. She jabbed the typewriter keys viciously, uncaring now whether she made mistakes or not, muttering to herself about male chauvinist pigs and arrogant lawyers.

The door to Sloan's office suddenly flew open, and a distraught Leonie came stumbling out. She had a filmy white handkerchief pressed to her mouth and was sobbing. Dark streaks of black mascara stained her cheeks.

She gave Sarah a stricken look, opened her mouth to say something, then groaned and tottered off down the hall on her spike heels.

I'll be damned if I'll run after her and hold her hand, Sarah thought, after the way she looked at me. Besides, if she didn't get busy on those notes she'd be there all night.

She resumed her typing, but in a few moments she stopped, aware that Sloan, still seated at his desk, was staring at her through the open door.

What does he want now? she wondered. She looked at him over her typewriter and could hardly believe her eyes. He was actually grinning at her, a fatuous, self-satisfied smirk that made her want to get up and smack him. After that dreadful scene, he sat there like the cat that swallowed the canary, looking so pleased with himself that she could cheerfully have murdered him.

'You can go home, now, Kincaid,' he said pleasantly.

She managed to keep the surprise from showing in her face and pointed to her notebook.

'I thought you needed this by eight

o'clock in the morning.' Her voice was tight with the effort to control herself.

He laughed shortly, then stood up and stretched widely, flexing the muscles of his long arms. He walked towards her until his large frame filled the doorway, his hands braced on either side, still smirking, leaning slightly forward.

'Merely a ploy,' he announced cheerfully. 'Call it a defensive manoeuvre. I wanted you here for protection.'

'You didn't look as though you needed protection,' she countered in a dry tone.

He merely shrugged and glanced out the window. 'It's raining,' he said.

'Yes, I know.'

He gave her a sharp look. 'It's late. You've missed your train.'

Sarah nodded and stood up, straightening her desk. 'There's another one in half an hour.'

'I'll drive you home,' he announced. 'Where do you live?'

She looked at him unable this time to keep the surprise from showing on her face.

Their eyes met, and he held her gaze in his for several seconds. Sarah was suddenly intensely aware that they were alone in the office. It was strangely silent, with none of the normal sounds of a busy law firm. No phones rang, no typewriters clacked, no voices were raised.

She looked away. 'It's all right, I don't mind taking the train.' She made her voice brisk and businesslike to mask the uncomfortable feeling their isolation gave her.

'Don't argue with me, Kincaid,' he said brusquely. He ran a hand through his thick hair. 'Why do women always have to argue?' It was a statement more than a question. 'Now tell me where you live.'

Sarah had to smile. It was typical of him and their relationship that she had worked closely with him for almost five years and he didn't even know where she lived. She wasn't sure she wanted him to, but knew it was useless to protest.

'I live in Berkeley,' she said at last. 'Near the university campus.'

He grabbed his raincoat off the hook on the back of the door. Then he switched the light off in his office and turned back to her. She was still standing by her desk.

'Come on, then, Kincaid, let's get going. I'm parked just across the street. You'll need a raincoat.'

'I don't have a raincoat,' she said.

He raised his eyebrows and gave her a mocking look. 'I can't believe it—the efficient Mrs Kincaid coming out without a raincoat! What's the world coming to?'

'It was quite nice out when I left for work this morning,' she said defensively.

'Yes, but I've noticed you're usually prepared for any contingency,' he said in a more serious tone. 'I've come to count on that.'

Sarah couldn't believe her ears. In five years it was the closest he'd come to a compliment. Since she always received a healthy raise in salary twice a year and a substantial bonus at Christmas, she assumed he was satisfied with her work, and had contented herself with that. Hearing even that slight praise from him, though, made all the difference, and she felt her earlier anger evaporate.

She started to follow him out of the office and was reaching to switch off the light when he turned back to her.

'Oh, by the way, make a note to send Leonie . . .'

'I know,' she interrupted. 'Two dozen red roses.'

He grinned. 'You see what I mean? Prepared for any contingency!'

She waited for him under the covered entrance to the building while he picked up his car, and as she stood shivering a little in the cold damp night air, she made a mental note to herself about the roses for Leonie. She had performed this task several times in the past. Although Sloan kept his personal life entirely separate from the office, even to the point of ending his affair with Leonie because she dared to break his iron rule about visitors, he hated to shop, and had early on delegated that ritual to her.

He didn't even bother to tell Sarah any more what to put on the card, and she had learned through practice to imitate his firm slashing handwriting. 'Fond memories, no regrets,' the card always said.

As she stood waiting for him, listening to the rain pattering on the sidewalk, the swish of the traffic going by on the wet streets, the clang of a cable car climbing a nearby hill, she wondered how those women felt when they received that brief message from a man they had loved.

Or had any of them really loved him? He was physically overpowering, she had to admit, even though she herself had managed to withstand his compelling magnetism. He was also quite a catch, still a bachelor at the age of thirty-six, at the top of his profession, and quite wealthy, she knew from doing his income tax returns every year. Not only did he command high fees, but he invested wisely, if a trifle riskily, and he came from an old California family with inherited money in the background.

As she thought now of Leonie and the roses she would send her tomorrow, it occurred to her for the first time that all Sloan's women had fitted the same pattern. Aristocratic, tall, beautifully if artificially groomed, dressed in the latest expensive fashions, they were all brunettes. Only the colour of their eyes varied.

Without thinking, Sarah put a hand to her own honey-gold hair, a little damp and frizzing slightly in the rain-soaked air, and thought she was as far removed from his ideal woman as it was possible to get.

She was grateful that she wasn't his type, and grateful, too, that she was immune to his impressive charms. She had Derek to thank for that, she thought bitterly, his one legacy to her that she valued. Derek's appeal had been almost as overpowering as Sloan's, and he had taught her well in their brief marriage the terrible suffering that resulted from flying too near such an irresistible flame.

Sloan's car appeared at the kerb, a Mercedes, sleek and dark, just like its owner. The passenger door opened, lighting up the interior, and Sarah saw Sloan leaning across the seat, his hand pushing the door open, an impatient expression on his lean dark face.

'Come on, Kincaid, hurry up,' he called. 'This is a bus zone.'

She jumped inside and slammed the door and before she had settled herself on the comfortable leather-upholstered seat, the car had zoomed off, merging smoothly into the flow of traffic. It was warm and cosy inside the car. It smelled of leather, cigarette smoke and a vague familiar scent she always associated with Sloan, clean and musky, a blend of light aftershave and fine woollen, an indefinably male scent.

Sloan drove as he did everything else, with competent ease and no wasted motion. She was glad to see that unlike Derek he seemed to have no need to prove his masculinity behind the wheel of a car. He neither drove too fast nor darted in and out of traffic, and when a noisy red sports car cut in front of him, narrowly missing his front bumper, he only laughed, almost as though he pitied such reckless stupidity.

'We'll stop and get something to eat on the other side of the bridge,' he announced as they drove up the ramp on to the Bay Bridge, connecting Oakland and San Francisco.

Just like that, Sarah thought wryly. It was so like him. No, 'Do you have plans for dinner,' or 'Are you hungry?' She didn't say anything, and he obviously took her silence for assent. Why argue? she thought resignedly.

She gazed around at the lights of the City—always spoken as if it had a capital C by Bay Area residents—behind them and smiled to herself. She settled back comfortably, enjoying the ride, and enjoying, more than she would have thought possible, the pleasant sensation of riding in a warm powerful car on a rainy night with an attractive man, the lights from the boats on the dark bay blinking all around them as they crossed the majestic bridge.

They had a quick meal at a small restaurant in Oakland. During dinner, Sloan filled her in on the Alvarez case, and their conversation was entirely limited to business. His attitude towards her here in the comfortable lounge where he preferred to eat was no different from what it was in the office, even though there were candles on the table and soft music in the background.

Sarah enjoyed her dinner. It was a relaxing atmosphere, the padded banquette comfortable, the lights dim, and a cheery fire blazing in a brick fireplace nearby.

After dinner, Sloan lit a thin cigar and ordered a brandy. As he smoked, he leaned his head back on the padded banquette and closed his eyes briefly. The little lines at the corners were more deeply etched than usual, and his face was drawn. In the intimate setting, Sarah felt suddenly closer to him than she ever had before.

'You look tired,' she said softly. It was the nearest she had ever come to a personal remark, and she instantly regretted it when his eyes snapped open and he frowned at her.

'I'm never tired,' he announced firmly.

She suppressed a smile. 'No, of course not,' she murmured. 'Sorry.'

He untangled his long legs from under the table and rose to his feet.

'However, since I'm sure you're anxious to get home, perhaps we'd better go. After all, it is Friday.' He picked up the check and glanced at it, then threw some bills down on the table. 'Your husband will be wondering what's happened to you.'

Sarah hesitated, about to remind him that she had no husband, but decided against it. He knew perfectly well, she thought as she followed him out to the car, that Derek had died shortly after she had started working for him. He just didn't want to remember.

It was another of Sloan Sheridan's ironclad rules that he only hired married women as his secretary. Apparently at some point in the distant past, he had become romantically involved with an unattached secretary and it had led to disaster. He allowed nothing to interfere with his work, and in order to forestall a repetition of that unhappy episode, made married status an absolute requirement in hiring.

Well, I was married when he hired me, Sarah thought as she directed him to her little house in the hills overlooking the Berkeley campus. I didn't lie. I can't help it if he chooses to overlook the fact that I shortly afterwards became a widow.

With his rigidly compartmentalised mind, he was able conveniently to forget anything that might disturb the efficient running of his office. Sarah had taken great pains, especially after Derek was killed, to dress and act as unprovocatively as possible, to keep a low profile and fade into the background so as not to arouse Sloan's apprehensions about her.

She loved her job. It filled the emptiness of her life as nothing else could. After Derek had nearly destroyed her, she had made up her mind that she would never trust her judgment about men again. So accustomed had she become to the dim shadowy image she projected at the office that it no longer felt like a lie, but an expression of her true nature.

Sloan dropped her off in front of her house. The rain had stopped and a pale moon appeared in the night sky. She opened the door and turned to him.

'Thank you very much for the lift,' she said primly. 'And the dinner.'

He nodded curtly. 'Not at all.'

As she walked up the winding path to her front door, Sarah realised that he was waiting at the kerb until she was safely inside the dark house, and hurried her steps a little so as not to keep him.

She unlocked the door, stepped inside and turned on the porchlight. Then she raised an arm and heard the powerful car zoom off into the darkness.

Sarah went into her bedroom. It was still early, only seven-thirty. She'd shower and watch a little television or listen to music, she decided.

The house was cold. She turned on the heat, but it didn't seem to help. As she stood in front of the full-length mirror on her closet door, surveying her drab, somewhat woebegone appearance, a sudden wave of loneliness swept over her.

I'm only twenty-six years old, she thought wildly, and I look years older. She wished irrelevantly that she hadn't had dinner with Sloan that night, that he hadn't driven her home. The silence and emptiness of her house seemed almost unbearable now after his vivid presence in the restaurant and in the car.

That's really something, she thought, grimacing at her reflection, when I prefer the company of a man like Sloan Sheridan to solitude! Better get a grip on yourself, my girl. You're losing your mind.

Firmly she took off her useless glasses and

unpinned her hair, letting it fall loosely around her shoulders. She took off the black suit, reminding herself to brush and press it the next day, and put the white blouse in the laundry hamper.

Then, with only her bra and half-slip on, her long honey-coloured hair framing her face, she began to feel somewhat reassured. She was an attractive woman, she knew, her tall figure firm and slim, her greenish hazel eyes clear, her skin smooth. If she wanted, she thought defiantly, she could give a woman like Leonie a run for her money.

And there would go her job, she realised, making a wry face at herself. She had made her decision, and she'd stick to it. Love was too much trouble. The wave of depression had passed. She liked her life as it was. Vaguely she blamed Sloan Sheridan for her moment of weakness. If he hadn't kept her late to help him with his silly love affair, if he hadn't insisted on driving her home, feeding her, if . . .

Then she laughed out loud and walked

into the bathroom, pinning her hair up as she went. If he only knew, she thought, as she stepped into the shower, what went on in the head of his prim secretary!

CHAPTER TWO

On Monday, Sarah sent the two dozen red roses with the standard note to Leonie, and wondered idly who would be next in line. During the week she finished her Christmas list and did most of her shopping, braving the crowded stores and biting cold at night after work, when the stores stayed open.

On the weekend before Christmas she drove to her parents' house in the Piedmont district of Oakland, overlooking San Francisco Bay, the City and the surrounding towns. The dinner was to welcome her sister Margaret, up from Santa Barbara for the holidays with Sarah's three-year-old nephew, Billy. Robert, Margaret's husband, was to fly up the next day.

'Well, Sadie,' her father was saying to her across the table over coffee, 'how's the job?'

'Oh, Dad,' Sarah protested, 'the names I get saddled with! You insist on calling me Sadie, and Sloan calls me Kincaid!'

Her father, a tall dignified-looking man with greying hair and a twinkle in his eye, grinned at her.

'Why, I've always called you Sadie.'

'Yes, I know. It makes me sound like a barmaid.'

'Why does Mr Sheridan call you Kincaid, dear?' her mother asked. 'Doesn't he know you took your maiden name back after Derek was killed?'

Sarah gave her a wry look. 'Sloan Sheridan is a law unto himself. He hasn't even acknowledged yet that Derek is dead. Besides, I don't want anyone at work to know I'm related to Dean John Tennant of the University Law School.'

Her father looked hurt. 'Why, Sadie, are you ashamed of me?'

She smiled at him with affection and respect. As Dean of the Law School, he was a prominent figure in Bay Area legal circles, a fact she kept well hidden from her co-workers.

'Of course not, Dad. I just don't want anyone to accuse me of using your influence. Especially Sloan.'

'How is the ogre?' he asked, chuckling. Sloan Sheridan had been one of his star pupils and he followed his rising career with almost paternal interest.

Sarah shrugged and made a face. 'The same. Like the winds and the tides, Sloan Sheridan never changes.'

'You make him sound more like a force of nature than a man,' her mother remarked lightly.

'Sometimes I think he is,' Sarah replied.

'I think he sounds disgusting,' commented Margaret in an ugly tone.

Sarah gave her sister a sharp look. Margaret had been strangely subdued since her arrival that afternoon. She was ordinarily the vivacious, outgoing one of the two sisters, with auburn hair and bright green eyes, while Sarah was more reserved and withdrawn.

'Oh, no, Margaret,' she protested now. 'He's a fine lawyer and, in his way, a high-principled man. He just likes to have things his own way.'

'Like most men,' Margaret commented on a sour note.

'Hey now, I resent that!' her father protested.

Margaret managed a weak smile. 'Oh, not you, Dad.'

There was a short silence then, and Sarah wondered what in the world was wrong with Margaret. They'd have to have a talk later.

'Is he married?' her mother asked.

Sarah turned to her. 'Who, Sloan? Oh, no. I don't think the woman's been born who could tame him. Why do you ask?'

Her mother reddened slightly. 'Well, dear, I was just thinking. I mean, Derek has been dead four years now, and you're a very attractive girl.'

Sarah couldn't help herself. She burst out laughing. 'Oh, Mother, you don't know

what you're saying! Sloan would fire me on
the spot if it once penetrated that I no
longer even have a husband, much less saw
him as potential husband material.'

Her mother gave her a puzzled look. 'You
mean he doesn't know about Derek?'

'Oh, he knows, all right. He couldn't help
but know. After all, it was in all the
newspapers and, I'm sure, the talk of the
office for days when Derek ran his car off
that cliff.'

She shuddered now as she remembered
the headlines. 'Prominent Bay Area
Stockbroker Killed,' and the story below
that made it quite clear, albeit in veiled
language, that Derek Kincaid had not only
been drunk, but was with his current flame
at the time of the accident.

'Well then,' her mother began. But Sarah
interrupted.

'He just doesn't want to admit that his
secretary is unmarried,' she explained. 'It's
another one of his rules.'

Her mother gave her a speculative look.

'Well, dear, I still say you're a very pretty girl, and he sounds quite eligible to me.'

About as eligible as typhoid, Sarah thought drily. She didn't bother to explain to her mother that she deliberately made herself unappealing in the office. She would never understand. Safely and happily married to a kind, loving man for thirty years, it was beyond her comprehension why marriage wasn't every woman's dream.

Besides, Sarah dropped her severe image away from the office. She still preferred tailored clothes, but with softer lines and more colourful materials. She allowed her heavy mane of hair to hang loose, or held back from her face with a wide band, and discarded the glasses she didn't need.

She changed the subject adroitly and soon the conversation had gone off on a different tack.

After dinner, while Margaret went to unpack and settle Billy for the night, Sarah helped her mother clear the table and do up the dishes.

Then, when her parents had settled in front of the fire for their nightly game of backgammon, she went down the hall to the bedroom wing to her sister's old room.

She rapped lightly on the door. There was no answer, and she knocked again, more loudly this time.

'Come in,' came a weary voice.

Sarah opened the door and went inside. The room was dark, curtains drawn, but by the light spilling in from the hall she could see her sister sitting on the edge of the bed, her shoulders slumped.

Sarah hesitated, debating whether she shouldn't leave her alone. Margaret was a proud, self-assured woman who always seemed in complete control of her life. Surely she would resent any intrusion from her younger sister.

'Sorry to disturb you,' Sarah said, her hand still on the doorknob. 'We can talk later if you like.'

Margaret turned around, and Sarah was shocked to see that she had been crying.

'No, come on in. I need to talk to someone. I was waiting for you, hoping you'd come.' She switched on the bedside lamp.

Sarah stepped inside and shut the door. Trying to avoid looking at her sister's ravaged face, she crossed over to the dressing table and sat down on the bench.

'Did you get Billy safely tucked away?' she asked at last.

'Yes. He's a docile little boy.' Margaret smiled weakly and looked at Sarah. 'Something like you were when we were children.' She sighed. 'I was the troublesome one.'

Sarah didn't know what to reply to that. Neither of them could help their own natures. She well remembered Margaret's childhood tantrums, her insistence on getting her own way, but never thought of comparing it to her own more pliant personality. They were just different, that was all, with different virtues, different flaws.

There was another long silence. Finally, Margaret got up from the bed and went to the window. She pulled the curtain aside and stood staring out into the darkness for a long time.

'I'm leaving Robert,' she said at last.

Sarah half rose from the bench, then sat back down. 'Oh, no!' she protested. 'Why?'

Margaret turned to face her then, her lovely features twisted and ugly in a parody of a smile.

'Tell me, Sarah, how did you feel when you first found out Derek had been unfaithful to you?'

Sarah's eyes filled with tears, tears of pity for her sister, but also, she had to admit, for herself and the bitter memories the conversation was evoking.

'I felt—betrayed,' she said at last in a shaky voice. She raised a hand. 'Margaret, I'm so sorry. I can hardly believe it of Robert.'

Her sister's husband was a solid, stable, almost dull man, a prominent Santa Barbara doctor who took his responsibilities—and his reputation—very seriously.

'I don't want your sympathy,' Margaret snapped. 'Just tell me what to do. What did you do?'

'Well,' Sarah began slowly, 'the first thing to do is make sure you're right. In my case there was no room for doubt. I caught them in bed.'

She closed her eyes, and could see once again Derek's dark head on the pillow of *her* bed, the blonde girl lying next to him, both naked under the thin sheet.

Margaret was pacing now, so immersed in her own trouble she didn't even notice the pain the conversation was causing her sister.

'Well, of course, Robert is too cautious to get caught doing anything so flagrant.' Her voice was clipped and with a bitter tone.

'Then how do you know?' Sarah asked. 'How can you be so sure?'

'Oh, I know he's seeing someone—a pathetic little widow, one of his patients. He tells me he's only being kind to her, but I know the signs. He's hiding something from me, and I won't stand for it.' She whirled to face Sarah, her body rigid, fists clenched at her sides, her green eyes blazing. 'I won't stand for it!'

Sarah could only stare at her. She had always felt dominated by her volatile older sister. Margaret had been the star of the family, with a pack of worshipful men surrounding her wherever she went. Sarah's was a quieter beauty, not so flamboyant as her sister's, and with her reserved nature she had been glad to fade into the background and let Margaret take the centre of the stage.

But we're grown women now, she thought to herself, watching her angry sister, not children. She stood up and gave Margaret a long, cool look.

'I think you're overreacting, Margaret,' she said calmly. 'Robert is a good man, a wonderful husband and father. You have Billy to think of. Don't jump to conclusions on so little evidence. You'll be very sorry if you leave him now without at least talking it over, giving him a chance to explain.'

'And what about you?' Margaret spat at her. 'Did you give Derek a chance to explain? You left him, after all.'

'It's not the same thing at all,' Sarah replied evenly. 'We had no children. We'd only been married a few months. Derek was drinking too much.' She looked away. 'And I found out later that it had happened before, that he never had been, never intended to be faithful to me.'

Then Margaret burst into tears and flung herself down on the bed. Sarah went over and sat down beside her, stroking her long bright hair. As the sobs subsided, Sarah withdrew her hand and sat silently beside her sister for a long time.

Finally she said, 'You still love him, don't you?' Margaret got out a strangled, 'Yes.' Sarah smiled. 'Then talk to him. Even if it's what you suspect, you can forgive him one mistake, can't you?'

'I don't see why!' Margaret wailed.

'Because of Billy. Because of the life you've built together. And because you love him.'

Margaret sat up, calmer now. 'You loved Derek.' Her voice was accusing.

Sarah shook her head. 'No—I don't think so now. I was fascinated by him, his good looks, his personal magnetism. But it was never love.' She turned and gave Margaret a fierce look. 'I can tell you this. If Derek and I had had what you and Robert have, no power on earth could have induced me to give it up.'

Driving home alone that night through the dark streets, Sarah thought over the conversation with her sister. She hoped something of what she had said would penetrate. She understood how Margaret felt. Betrayal of a loved one was always a blow. Looking back on her own experience with Derek, she wondered now how she had ever lived through it.

She'd been so young when they married,

barely twenty-one, and totally swept off her feet by the tall dark man who had, she realised now, only married her because she wouldn't go to bed with him otherwise.

He had never had any intention of being faithful to her, and when she left him, six months after their wedding, neither of them wanted a divorce. Their marital status was protection for them both, hers because she had vowed she would never be taken in like that again, and Derek's so that he could pursue his amorous adventures without the threat of another marriage.

Sarah tossed and turned on her bed that night, unable to sleep. The conversation with Margaret had raked up old memories she thought had been laid to rest. She knew she had a lot to be grateful for—an interesting job that paid well, freedom to do as she liked with her life, her home, her family, a few close friends.

As Derek's legal widow, she had inherited the house and was the beneficiary of a small insurance policy. There had been little cash;

Derek had had expensive tastes and woman-chasing cost money. Still, she was relatively well-off financially.

Finally, she drifted into a troubled sleep. The next day was Sunday and she could stay in bed as long as she liked. She had pushed her unhappy marriage out of her mind once, and she could do it again. It had hardly been a marriage, anyway.

The following Friday was the office Christmas party. Sarah never really enjoyed these annual orgies when the office closed at noon, the drink flowed freely, and a lot of people made fools of themselves who were very sorry about it later.

Sarah always put in a token appearance. She didn't want her reserve to be misinterpreted as snobbery. The food, catered by one of San Francisco's most exclusive restaurants, was always superb, and usually she would have one drink, eat with a group of older secretaries and leave by three o'clock.

This year, however, the younger lawyers had prevailed upon the managing partner to provide music and dancing. The enormous work room had been decorated, all the office machines and tables pushed aside, and someone had brought a record player.

After consuming her one drink and plateful of delicious food, Sarah stood for a moment on the sidelines with the managing partner's secretary watching the dancers. It was now that the serious drinking would begin, sometimes lasting until midnight, and Sarah planned to make a quiet exit soon.

She turned to the woman at her side, a tall, stiffly-corseted spinster with iron-grey hair and a stern manner. Viola Manners took her position as senior secretary quite seriously, and considered she had an ally in the reserved Sarah in her disapproval of the raucous festivities.

'It looks as though everyone is having a good time,' Sarah commented.

'Dancing!' Viola snorted. 'What next! I

shudder to think.' She gestured to a couple in the middle of the floor who were clinging together without regard to the beat of the music. 'That's what comes of hiring women lawyers,' she sniffed.

Sarah smiled. The noise from the stereo and voices raised in celebration was deafening. The room was crowded. Everyone had finished eating by now, and the music blaring from the work room had attracted them like a magnet.

'Aren't the decorations lovely?' she remarked, hoping to distract the older woman from her quite vocal disapproval. 'The girls worked late last night and all morning long to get it ready.'

There were greens festooned on the walls with bright red ribbons. The plastic Christmas tree had been set up in a corner and strung with bright lights. Mistletoe hung in bunches from the light fixtures, and a giant Santa Claus poster was tacked on the wall above the copying machine.

Viola was shaking her head slowly from

side to side. 'Look at those girls,' she remarked sadly. 'The way they get themselves up. After all, it is still a business office, even if it's Christmas.'

Sarah glanced around the crowded room. Every woman there, from the youngest file clerk to old Mrs Carruthers, the bookkeeper, seemed to be dressed in some vibrant colour. She looked at Viola Manners, stiff in her severe brown woollen dress, then down at her own grey flannel suit. Her one concession to the party atmosphere had been a small cluster of artificial roses on the lapel of her suit jacket.

Suddenly she saw herself and Viola as the others must view them, and felt decidedly uncomfortable. Two old bags, she thought, standing on the sidelines with frowns of disapproval and drab clothes while everyone else had a good time.

But I'm not old, she cried to herself, and felt the sudden wild impulse to fling herself on the dance floor and ask the first man she saw to dance with her.

Then she recovered herself. I've got to get out of here, she thought. Things were getting out of hand. The music seemed louder, the voices more raucous, the dancing more uninhibited, and someone had turned off the overhead lights, leaving only the dim glow of a desk lamp to illuminate the crowded room.

Murmuring something inaudible to Viola, Sarah turned to go, and almost crashed into Warren Langley. There was a wide grin on his boyish face, and he was holding a drink in either hand.

'Here,' he said, thrusting one of the glasses at her. She was so startled that she reached out for it instinctively and took it from him. 'Merry Christmas,' he cried, and leaned over to kiss her loudly on the cheek.

She was too surprised to be offended at this unexpected familiarity, and he was smiling at her so happily she didn't have the heart to put him in his place. After all, she thought, it was Christmas. She smiled at him.

'That's better,' he said with satisfaction. 'For a minute there I thought you and Ma Manners were going to find axes and chop up the saloon, like the old temperance ladies!'

Sarah was stung. A reserved, distant image in the office was one thing, being linked with Viola as a damper on the party quite another. She gave Warren a steely look through her glasses and took a long swallow of her drink.

His eyes widened. 'Good girl,' he remarked appreciatively. 'Now, finish your drink and we'll dance.'

A little voice in her head warned Sarah she should turn and march out, but by now it was too late. She wanted to stay, wanted to enjoy herself. All the others were so far gone in their own pursuit of pleasure that no one would pay any attention to her. It was only a dance, for heaven's sake. One dance and she'd go home.

'All right,' she said. She took another swallow of her drink and set the glass down on the counter, and the next thing she knew she was in Warren's arms and he was leading her out on to the dance floor.

It had been so long since she'd danced that she stumbled a little at first, but Warren held her tightly and after a few awkward moves her body began to flow naturally with the music. Warren was a strong leader and didn't try any fancy steps, and soon she began to enjoy herself.

When the music ended, she smiled at Warren and drew away from him. It really was time she went home, she decided, but he held her securely by her arms. She looked up at him.

'I've got to go,' she said firmly, pulling away from him.

He was staring down at her, a speculative look in his blue eyes. 'You know,' he said slowly, reaching one hand up to take hold of her glasses, 'you don't need these on when you're dancing.'

He pulled the glasses off and put them in his jacket pocket, disturbing her neat chignon as he did so, so that a few strands of long hair came loose. Sarah began to feel alarmed. Warren had obviously had a little too much to drink. The last thing she wanted was to create a scene, but things were getting out of hand.

As she gazed past Warren's shoulder, stalling for time, trying to think of the best way to handle the sticky situation, her glance fell on Viola Manners, still standing, stiff and disapproving, at the door.

Well, Sarah thought resignedly. I'm damned if I do and damned if I don't. If I insist on leaving I'll be tarred with that brush, and if I stay I'll jeopardise my precious image.

She looked back at Warren, who was openly leering at her now. It was terribly hot in the crowded room, and she could feel beads of perspiration forming on her forehead. She glanced around and saw that most of the men had discarded their jackets and rolled up their shirtsleeves. A few had taken off their ties. In the dim corners she

could see couples locked together in passionate embraces, and she knew that on
Monday morning there would be many red
faces.

'It's too warm in here,' she said at last. 'I
really must go now.'

To her relieved amazement, Warren
released her instantly, but as she turned
away from him, she felt her jacket being
pulled off her shoulders and down her arms.
His firm arm came back around her waist,
pulling her towards him. He flung her jacket
in a pile on one of the chairs and put his
other arm around her.

'There,' he said, 'is that better?'

It was the last straw. Sarah was growing
really angry now. She had to put a stop to
this immediately. She drew stiffly away
from him and pushed at his chest.

'Stop it right now, Warren,' she said in a
cold voice, 'or I'll make such a scene you
won't want to show your face in here on
Monday morning!'

Warren drew back, his eyes wide, his

mouth open, shocked surprise on every feature. 'I was only having some fun,' he said in a bewildered tone.

'Well, the fun's over,' she said firmly. 'Now, let me go.'

His eyes narrowed at her then and he flushed deeply. 'Excuse me,' he said nastily. 'I guess I forgot for a minute that I was dealing with an iceberg, not a woman.'

Then, as she watched him unbelievingly, he leaned forward and she knew he intended to kiss her. Trembling with anger, she instinctively raised her hand to hit him, when she felt herself whirled around and pulled firmly up against a hard masculine chest.

'I've told you before, Langley,' she heard Sloan Sheridan's voice say in a low clipped tone, 'leave my secretary alone!'

Then, in a daze, she was swept away in his arms and propelled towards the door, his firm hold on her never lessening for an instant. In all the years she had worked for him, he had never even touched her before, much less held her so close, and her heart started to pound uncontrollably. His strong thighs pushed against hers and the rough material of his jacket brushed against her cheek as his long arms firmly grasped her to him.

'Can't you stay out of trouble for five minutes?' he muttered, still propelling her inexorably before him with his long strides.

She looked up at him and opened her mouth to protest her injured innocence, but the look of anger and contempt on his face stopped her cold. They danced through the doorway and down the silent corridor to an empty office. The music from the dance floor faded behind them, then stopped altogether when he shoved her inside the office and kicked the door shut.

He grabbed her by the shoulders now, his dark eyes smouldering, his mouth set and grim. He shook her roughly.

'Look at you!' he growled at her, his eyes raking her body up and down. 'Your hair's a mess, your glasses are God knows where, and you're half undressed!'

Sarah had recovered from her first shock and was beginning to grow angry. 'Half undressed?' she cried. 'I have my jacket off, for heaven's sake! Don't be ridiculous!'

She glanced down and saw that the top button of her silk blouse had come undone in the struggle with Warren, revealing the white lace of her slip and a good portion of deep cleavage between her breasts. She flushed deeply and struggled to free herself so she could do up her blouse, but his grip on her only tightened. Nobody called Sloan Sheridan ridiculous, she knew, especially a mere secretary. Well, she thought fatalistically, there goes my job. Might as well go all the way.

She glared up at him. 'I don't know what gives you the right to order me around, anyway. I'm on my own time. Now, let me go—you're hurting me!'

To her surprise, he released her. His anger seemed to have vanished, and a strange, appraising look appeared on his face. He backed away and leaned his hips on the edge of the desk against the wall, folding his arms in front of him.

Suddenly he smiled, and his white even teeth flashed against his dark face. Sarah suppressed a little gasp. The smile transformed him, and she began to get an inkling of why women found him so irresistible.

'Well, well,' he drawled in an amused tone, 'the cool, unflappable Mrs Kincaid shows her claws at last! I never dreamed you had it in you.'

'You provoked me,' she muttered, still angry. Free from that iron grip at last, she hastily buttoned her blouse and tucked the stray strands of long hair back into her chignon.

She lifted her chin defiantly and gave him a cool stare. He was still grinning at her, his head cocked to one side. Sarah began to see the humour of the situation, and in spite of her annoyance, she found herself smiling back at him.

Their eyes met, and she watched the mocking amusement in those inscrutable black pools turn to a speculative intensity, saw him rise up slightly. She began to feel uncomfortably warm again, even though the little office was quite cool compared to the dance floor.

The swift certain conviction came to her that she was in far more danger from this tall dark man, poised like a panther about to strike, then she ever had been from Warren Langley. She saw the brooding look vanish as he got briskly to his feet and opened the door.

'Go and find your jacket,' he ordered in a clipped tone. 'I'll take you home.'

Sarah had regained her composure. The highly-charged moment had passed. It would never be repeated, she vowed sternly to herself. Any personal involvement with Sloan Sheridan would be madness, a disaster for her professionally and personally.

'No, thank you,' she said, her tone pleasant, but cool. She walked past him and out into the corridor. 'I'm meeting someone.' She gave him one level glance, and he nodded briefly.

She had trouble finding her jacket in the almost pitch dark work room. The crowd had thinned out considerably by now, and only the serious merrymakers remained. Someone had put a slow romantic tune on the record player, and Sarah kept her eyes firmly averted from the couples closely entangled together in the shadows.

She found her jacket at last in the same pile where Warren had tossed it earlier. As she slipped it on and strode purposefully back across the dance floor, she had a momentary qualm about the glasses he had slipped into his pocket. She shrugged and decided to let it go rather than hunt for him now. She didn't need them anyway.

She walked down the corridor, past the empty offices and through the reception room to the bank of elevators. Except for the lingering crowd in the work room, the whole office was deserted by now and quite still.

It wasn't until she punched the down button that she remembered her purse. She had left it in her office when she went to the party. 'Damn,' she muttered, and retraced her steps, past the work room again, down the hall to the far end of the floor and into her office.

At her desk, she reached down under her typewriter to retrieve her pusrse, then straightened up hurriedly when she heard Sloan's voice coming from the door between their offices.

'Have you decided to return to the party after all?' His tone was mocking.

Slowly she turned around to face him. He was lounging in the doorway, one long arm braced against the doorframe, the other holding a drink. He was still impeccably groomed and combed, and Sarah felt slovenly in comparison. Her glasses were gone, her hair still mussed, her jacket rumpled from the crush on the chair.

'Hardly,' she said, making her voice as cool as possible. 'I came to get my purse.'

She came around the desk. 'Goodnight, then, Sloan,' she said. 'Merry Christmas.'

As she passed by him, he reached out a hand and put it on her arm. She stiffened. Surely he didn't want her to work this evening? His touch unnerved her. Warily, she looked up at him.

His eyes were hooded and a lazy smile appeared on his face as he reached behind her and set his drink down on her desk. Then he took hold of her other arm and turned her around to face him.

'Merry Christmas, Kincaid,' he murmured, and the next thing she knew the dark head was bending toward her.

His kiss was gentle, almost brotherly, but at that first touch of his lips on hers, Sarah felt a tiny flame kindle in her heart. Instinctively, without thinking, her mouth softened under his, then parted slightly in response to the hardening pressure, and she could taste the liquor he had been drinking.

She felt Sloan's breath quicken as his hands left her arms and came around her.

She put her hands flat against his chest, and felt a sudden longing to run them inside his rough jacket, over the thin material of his shirt, to feel the powerful chest muscles, the beat of his heart. She gave an inward gasp as his hands began to move over her back, shuddering a little at the touch.

Then, abruptly, he drew away from her. His hands slid around to her arms, then dropped at his sides. He stared down at her for a brief second, his expression inscrutable. Then the moment was past. He glanced past her out the window.

'It's dark out,' he commented in a flat, distant tone. 'Are you sure you don't want a lift home? Won't your husband be worried about you?'

Sarah had recovered herself by now. She picked up her purse from the desk where she had dropped it, murmured her refusal of his offer of a ride, and without a backward glance, went off down the hall.

She could feel him watching her as she went and forced herself to walk as slowly and calmly as possible, her shoulders back, her head held high. Still, she was glad when she turned the corner at the end of the hall to get to the elevators and know she was out of his view.

This must never happen again, she vowed as she punched the elevator button. Let him think I'm married. It was another of his rules never to get involved with a married woman, and as his married secretary, she had double protection from him.

Still, she thought, riding down in the safety of the elevator, away from his disturbing presence, the kiss had had a definite impact on her. What in the world had got into him to do such a thing? It was an action so out of character for the man who kept his business and personal lives so rigidly separated.

Oh well, it's Christmas, after all, she told herself as she hurried through the well-lighted streets to catch her train. And he'd been drinking. By Monday it would be forgotten—she'd just have to see to that.

Any hint of a personal nature in their relationship, and she was certain, without question, that she'd be out of a job.

She knew she could easily get another one. Good, experienced legal secretaries were always in short supply, and as Sloan Sheridan's competent right hand for five years, she had acquired a high reputation in legal circles. Everyone knew how demanding and exacting he was.

But I don't want another job, she thought. She wanted to keep the one she had. A lawyer and his secretary, if they clicked, worked very closely together. It was almost like a marriage. She and Sloan Sheridan had established a splendid working relationship right from the beginning, and she had no desire to change that.

The train had crossed to the Oakland side of the Bay by now, and she glanced back at the lights outlining the bridge and winking on the steep hills of the City. The view at night always gave her a romantic feeling, and she unconsciously moved her fingers to her mouth where Sloan had kissed her, remembering the feel of his firm lips on hers, the tangy taste of the liquor on his breath, the faint smell of tobacco and mild aftershave on his rough cheek when he had held her in his arms.

The next stop was hers. She got up and started down the aisle, swaying a little with the momentum of the rushing train, promising herself once again to banish such thoughts about her boss from her mind for ever.

CHAPTER THREE

As it turned out, she needn't have worried. On Monday, after celebrating a subdued Christmas with her family, Sarah noticed that there was little talk of the office party at work. Those who had gone home early weren't interested, and those who had stayed wanted to forget.

Sloan barricaded himself all morning in his office with Warren Langley and Dr Alvarez. The trial would be coming up in August on the crowded court calendar. There had already been a lot of prurient publicity in the newspapers, and there would be a lot more now that Sloan Sheridan was involved.

Sarah knew from experience that he prepared such cases meticulously. He would depend heavily on Warren for research and legwork, but the strategy would be entirely under his own provenance. He would demand full authority to do things his way, but would also assume full responsibility if things went wrong.

At noon the three men broke for lunch. Without being told, Sarah had made reservations for them at the restaurant in the building. She could always cancel them at the last minute if Sloan decided to go somewhere else.

He came out of his office now and gave her an enquiring look. She handed him the sheaf of pink message slips. He leafed quickly through them, kept two and handed the rest back to her.

'You take care of those,' he said. 'You can stall Mrs Armitage and give Burnside the figures Warren came up with. The rest only need a little soothing. Are we booked downstairs for lunch?' She nodded. 'How about the Notice of Appearance in the Lonergan case?'

'It will be served and filed today,' she

replied in a crisp tone. 'I sent it out with the messenger this morning.'

He grunted and turned to join the other two men. Dr Alvarez looked drawn and harried. It was a terrible thing for a physician to be accused of such a crime, Sarah thought, even more so when she knew he was innocent. It was another of Sloan's rules never to take a case he didn't believe in, and it didn't even occur to Sarah to question his judgment.

Warren stayed behind as Sloan and the doctor walked slowly down the corridor, deep in quiet conversation. When they were out of earshot, he turned to Sarah and gave her a sheepish look. He reached in his jacket pocket, pulled out a pair of glasses and handed them to her.

'Sorry if I was out of line at the party on Friday, Sarah,' he mumbled. 'I had a little too much Christmas cheer.'

Sarah took the glasses from him. 'Not at all,' she said mildly. 'It was Christmas, after all.'

TWO DOZEN RED ROSES

She turned back to her work, but he lingered. She glanced up at him questioningly and he grinned.

'I even cleaned them for you!' She didn't reply. 'I noticed they were plain glass,' he went on. 'You don't even need them.'

'You're mistaken,' she said evenly. 'Some corrections are not that apparent.'

He shrugged. 'Have it your way.' He leaned down. 'I just got to wondering why a beautiful girl like you goes out of her way to be as unattractive as possible.' His face was quite close to hers. 'I wasn't so drunk Friday that I didn't notice that.'

A voice rang out from the other end of the corridor. 'Coming, Langley? We haven't got all day.'

It was Sloan. Warren straightened up and hurried out of the office, and Sarah smiled to herself. With the formidable Sloan Sheridan always hovering in the background, she didn't believe she had anything to fear from Warren Langley's probing.

Sloan was just as concerned as she was to sustain her touch-me-not image.

The days and weeks passed quickly, and soon it was spring. The cherry blossoms were ablaze in the Japanese tea garden in Golden Gate Park, and although the morning fogs still blanketed the whole Bay Area, by noon the streets of San Francisco were teeming with hatless, coatless pedestrians.

Sarah spent one whole weekend putting away her heavy winter clothes, zipping the woollen suits and coats into mothproof garment bags, polishing her sturdy, serviceable dark pumps and putting shoe trees in them. She surveyed her spring wardrobe.

There really wasn't much difference between them, she thought a little sadly as she transferred the lighter weight suits from the spare bedroom closet to her own. She made only a few concessions to the warmer weather. The neutral tones were lighter in colour, the materials gabardine or poplin instead of wool, and the bone-coloured shoes had a slightly higher heel.

Somehow, gazing dolefully at her colourless wardrobe on Sunday afternoon, the sunshine streaming in her bedroom window, the birds chirping gloriously in the sprawling pepper tree at the side of the house, Sarah suddenly thought about the office Christmas party.

She wondered again what had got into Sloan to kiss her like that. She certainly hadn't invited it. Since then it had been business as usual at the office. The incident had never been referred to again, and Sarah assumed Sloan had forgotten all about it.

That suits me, she said to herself as she stood gazing at her reflection in the mirror on her closet door. She had on a pair of well-worn, figure-hugging jeans and a white cotton shirt. Not a very sexy image, she thought, posing a little, but certainly more appealing than the office image she projected.

She lifted the heavy honey-gold hair in

her hand and held it loosely up on top of her head. What would happen, she wondered, if she showed up at the office one day with her hair loose, without her glasses, a really clever make-up job and a soft dress?

She laughed. Poor Sloan would either have a heart attack or fire her on the spot! She was only a piece of furniture to him, or at best an unassuming, characterless automaton, there to do his bidding, without question or argument. She could probably show up naked, and he wouldn't notice.

Still, she thought, letting the smooth hair fall again to her shoulders, since the Christmas party she had caught him several times looking at her in an odd way. Just last Monday she had been absorbed all morning in working out a complicated deed of trust for Mrs Armitage. At noon she had finally given up, bleary-eyed from the close work. She had taken her glasses off and stretched her aching shoulder muscles, when she happened to glance into Sloan's office.

He had been sitting leaning back in his

swivel chair, his long legs apart, feet planted on the floor, his hands making a pointed steeple under his chin. At first he only seemed to be deep in thought, gazing into space, pondering one of his knotty problems. She soon realised, however, that the dark gaze was fastened firmly on her.

Their eyes had met briefly, then his telephone had rung. He swivelled around in his chair to answer it, and the moment passed. Sarah had forgotten about it. It was an insignificant event not worth remembering.

Still, she had remembered. Why? And why had it come to her mind just now, in the train of her ruminative, idle thoughts about her appearance? Had the brief look meant anything to him?

Of course not, she told her reflection. Don't be so silly. She sighed and got back to work, muttering something to herself about spring fever.

Sarah usually took a walk at noon, then ate

her sandwich lunch in the firm's pleasant coffee room at quarter to one. By then the room had cleared out. Most of the other girls bolted their lunches in ten minutes, then left to go out shopping or on personal errands. Sarah liked the rest of the clerical staff and took great pains not to set herself above them in any way just because of her position as confidential secretary to the firm's most important lawyer.

Still, she was glad of the privacy during lunch after the usual morning spent coping with Sloan and his near-unreasonable expectations of her.

On the Wednesday following her wardrobe clean-up, however, she was feeling especially frazzled and decided not to go out at all during her lunch hour. The Alvarez case took up most of Sloan's time these days, leaving the burden of the rest of his caseload to Sarah to handle as best she could. It was becoming very wearing trying to think up new excuses for his clients as to why he wasn't returning their calls.

'Tell them anything you like,' he had barked at her when she raised the issue with him. 'Tell them I'm in hospital, or kidnapped, or gone to China. They only want their hands held, and you can do that as well as I can.'

She had spent the morning trying to soothe the indignant Mrs Armitage. 'Yes, Mrs Armitage, Mr Sheridan has gone over your quarterly reports from the bank very carefully. No, you really don't need to discuss it with him. Everything is in order.' And on and on.

By noon she felt fit only to eat her sandwich quietly by herself, curl up in one of the comfortable chairs and look through the magazines stacked on the coffee table.

When she entered the coffee room the six round tables were all occupied. She had hoped to get a table alone, but the others would probably be gone soon anyway. As she passed by them on her way to the refrigerator to get her sandwich, she saw that at least there were several empty chairs. She'd just have to share.

There were three girls sitting at the table she chose, one the receptionist, another a word-processing operator, and the third girl was Warren Langley's secretary. Their heads were close together over the table in animated conversation, and as she approached, she heard one of them pronounce her boss's name.

When she sat down, they glanced at her in unison and Ginger, Warren's secretary, stopped in mid-sentence. She was a small redhead, young, and with an irrepressible air of mischief about her. She giggled nervously.

'We were discussing your boss,' she announced with a hint of defiance in the tilt of her chin.

Sarah sighed. 'Don't mind me. There's nothing you could say about him that I haven't said—or thought—a dozen times myself.'

It was an accepted fact in the office that

Sloan Sheridan's secretary had a unique burden to carry. Several girls had threatened to quit when Sarah was on vacation and they had had to pick up on his work. She was, accordingly, viewed with respect and sympathy. No one wanted her job at any price.

The other three girls glanced conspiratorially at each other as Sarah unwrapped her sandwich and opened her carton of milk. Then Ginny, eyes dancing, leaned towards her.

'Have you heard, though, about his latest conquest?'

Sarah swallowed a bite of sandwich and took a drink of milk. She hated office gossip, but it was important to her to stay on good terms with the other girls. She smiled at Ginny.

'No, I haven't,' she said lightly.

'It's Ariel Boone,' Ginny whispered.

Sarah gave her a blank look. 'Who's Ariel Boone?'

Ginny sighed dramatically. 'Honestly,

Sarah, you're so out of it!' She leaned closer. 'Ariel Boone happens to be San Francisco's top fashion model. You see her picture in the paper all the time.'

'I'll take your word for it,' Sarah replied mildly, chewing on her sandwich. Her curiosity was aroused. 'How do you know she's involved with my boss?'

'Jack took me to the Top of the Mark for my birthday over the weekend, and we saw them there. From the way they were dancing, you could tell.' She giggled. 'I was afraid they weren't going to make it to the bedroom in time!'

Sarah felt a sharp prick of annoyance at this report. Why did Sloan always have to conduct his affairs in public? You'd think he'd have more concern for his professional image.

Nancy, the receptionist, spoke up now. 'I'd be willing to bet she was the one doing all the pawing.' Her tone was dry.

'Well,' Ginger hedged, 'she was pretty aggressive.'

'She calls him all the time,' Nancy went on, 'and he gave me strict orders never to put her through, to him or to you, Sarah.' She smiled. 'He said you've got better things to do with your time.'

Sarah had finished her lunch by now and was tidying up the debris. She glanced up to see all three girls looking at her speculatively.

'You know, Sarah,' Nancy began slowly, 'I've often wondered why you and Sloan . . . I mean, I know you like to keep a low-key image here at the office, but I saw you at the Christmas party dancing with Warren Langley, and you could be very attractive if you'd make a little effort.'

Sarah broke out laughing at that. 'Thanks, Nancy, but no thanks. Besides, Sloan only likes brunettes.'

Ginny snorted. 'I should think he'd be sick of all those glamour girls. He always drops them after a few months. He might like a change. And you'll have to admit, he's a gorgeous man.'

'Well then, Ginny,' Sarah said as she stood up, 'why don't you give it a try?' Her smile was kind, but firm.

Ginny opened her eyes wide. 'He terrifies me, that's why!'

All four girls laughed at that. As the secretary of Sloan's right-hand man, Ginny had had to bear the brunt of Sloan's demands when Sarah was gone from the office and had vowed that she was going to schedule her vacation the same time as Sarah's this year.

By mid-afternoon, Sarah's little office was uncomfortably warm. Since it was only April, the air-conditioning hadn't been turned on yet, in obedience to some arbitrary rule of the maintenance department, and the sun pouring in through the window made the room seem like an oven.

Sloan and Warren had gone all day over to Marin County for an interview at the District Attorney's office with Martha Layton and her mother, Dr Alvarez's accusers. It was getting on to four o'clock now, and Sarah doubted if they'd be back.

She took off the jacket of her beige gabardine suit and loosened the bright orange scarf around her neck, her one colourful concession to spring. She ran her hands over her hair, damp from perspiration, and felt the thick coil at the back of her neck, heavy and warm. She took out a few pins and pushed the chignon up higher on her head, sighing with relief as what air there was fanned her exposed skin.

That's better, she thought, and taking off the glasses that kept slipping down her nose, she turned her attention back to Mrs Armitage's quarterly reports.

An hour later, she was ready to call it a day. She closed the ledger book and got up from her chair. She'd be glad to get home and into a cool shower. She felt sticky all over. She went to the window and looked down at the street, twenty floors below.

In the distance she could see the sparkling blue of the Bay, the graceful bridge spanning it, the steep hills of the City, and the hordes of people below rushing to get home.

The insecurely attached chignon felt loose, and she raised her arms to fasten it when she heard voices behind her. Startled, she turned, her arms still stretched up to her head, and saw Sloan Sheridan and Warren Langley standing in the open doorway staring at her.

'You're back,' she mumbled, dropping her arms to her sides. She wondered why she felt a sudden urge to cover herself with her jacket, hanging on the back of her chair where she had left it, to jam her glasses back on her nose.

Don't be silly, she said to herself, recovering. She knew she looked perfectly respectable in her neat silk shirt, even if it was a little damp and clinging from the heat.

'I didn't expect you,' she murmured.

'Obviously,' Sloan muttered drily. He strode past her towards his office, leaving Warren still standing there gaping at Sarah.

At the door to his office, Sloan turned and glared at Warren. 'Are you going to stand there all day, Langley?' he barked, and Warren went off to his own office next door like a shot.

With the merest glance at Sarah, he held out a hand and she gave him the usual sheaf of pink message slips.

'How did it go today?' asked Sarah as he went through them.

'Not good,' he said curtly. 'That damned Layton girl looks fresh out of the convent. It's going to be a rough one. I've got to shake her story somehow.'

Sarah watched him carefully as he went through his messages. After what must have been a gruelling day, he looked as unruffled and imperturbable as ever. He was wearing a navy blue lightweight suit, with a still fresh white shirt and discreetly striped silk tie. His dark crisp hair, flecked here and there with grey, was a little longer than usual, but still neatly combed. He hadn't had time for his monthly haircut.

'Is it possible that Layton girl is telling the truth?' Sarah asked in a low voice.

His eyes flicked at her. 'No, damn it, she's not.' He rubbed his hand over the back of his neck. 'There's something wrong there, and I'm convinced it's the mother. I'll have to depose her.' He shrugged. 'I haven't found the key yet, but I will. I know it's there.'

He had sorted out the message slips by now. He kept some and threw the rest down on her desk.

'You can go home now, Kincaid. Deal with those tomorrow. I'll call these now myself.'

He went into his office, then, and shut the door. Sarah smiled to herself. Ariel Boone, she thought. Sloan never closed the door between their offices for business calls.

She got her purse out from under her typewriter, grabbed her jacket and set off down the hall. As she passed Warren Langley's office, she saw him standing in the doorway, looking hot and dishevelled.

He appeared to be waiting for her. He grinned.

'I don't know about you, but I could use a long cool drink. Join me?'

She hesitated. Ordinarily she would have made a polite excuse but she was hot and a drink sounded good before she had to face the ride home on the packed train. She also wanted to hear more about the interview with Martha Layton and her mother.

She looked at Warren, still grinning. He raised his hands in the air in a gesture of innocence. 'Just a drink downstairs. No passes—I promise!'

She laughed. 'All right. One drink.'

The lounge of the restaurant in the building was cool and dim. As Warren seated her at a table, she started to put her jacket on.

'Don't,' he said. 'Please don't. You look so nice with it off. Not nearly so formidable as usual.'

'Formidable?' Sarah asked in amazement. 'Me?' She set her jacket down beside her on the banquette. 'There's only room for one prima donna at our end of the office!'

Warren sat down across from her and after they had ordered their drinks, he gave her a thoughtful look.

'You don't like him much, do you?' he asked.

'Who? Our dauntless leader?' She thought the question over. 'I don't know. I like working for him, but if he has lovable qualities he keeps them well hidden from me. Of course, I don't think he tries very hard. He doesn't care whether I like him or not so long as I get the job done.'

Their drinks arrived then, and Sarah sipped gratefully at the long cool Tom Collins. She looked at Warren. 'Do you?' she asked. 'Like him?'

He leaned back in his chair, pondering for a moment. 'I think I do,' he said slowly. 'He's one hell of a lawyer, and certainly I admire him tremendously. I can't tell you how much he's taught me.' He laughed. 'Even though his lessons are sometimes painful!'

Sarah raised her eyebrows meaningfully. 'I know what you mean. He can get a bit rough at times.' She was feeling the effects of the drink now, and a wicked gleam appeared in the greenish hazel eyes. ' "I haven't got all day, Langley," ' she mimicked Sloan's curt tone. 'And "Get me that file, Kincaid." '

They both started laughing. Warren's hand came down on the table to cover hers, clutching at it in his merriment.

'Having fun, you two?' came a familiar voice.

The laughter died on their lips as they looked up in unison to see Sloan Sheridan looming over their table, tall and forbidding, his face like thunder. Sarah felt as though she had been caught with her hand in the cookie jar. Had he heard?

Warren jumped to his feet, overturning both their drinks as he pulled his hand abruptly away from Sarah's.

'Now look what you've done, Langley,' Sloan drawled nastily.

Sarah suppressed a nervous giggle. 'Oh, that's all right,' she said, barely able to contain herself, 'they're almost empty.'

'I can see that,' was Sloan's sarcastic reply. Sarah's mouth began to twitch, and he gave her a sharp look. 'What's so damned funny, Kincaid?'

It was then she noticed the tall, elegant brunette hovering behind Sloan, her hands clasped possessively on his arm. Ariel Boone, Sarah thought, and sobered up immediately.

'Nothing's funny,' she said coolly.

Sloan glanced from Warren to Sarah. 'What are you two doing here, anyway?'

Sarah was beginning to grow angry. She could feel Ariel Boone's amused superior eyes on her, taking in the ridiculous scene, and she was suddenly intensely aware of her own plain image. She felt awkward, out of her element, defensive. She *wished* Warren would get that hangdog expression off his face and quite goggling at the glamorous Ariel.

'Warren and I are having a drink,' Sarah

responded sweetly. 'Is there a law against it?' She wondered why he seemed so angry. They weren't in the office now.

'A pretty cosy drink, I'd say,' he commented drily, glancing down at her hand still resting on the table where Warren had dropped it like a hot potato at the first sound of Sloan's voice. 'For a married woman.'

'But Sarah's not . . .' Warren put in, his eyes wide.

Sarah shot him a warning look, and his mouth snapped shut. 'It's only a drink, for heaven's sake,' she broke in hurriedly to cover the awkwardness.

'Well, in that case,' Sloan drawled smoothly, 'you won't mind if we join you.' He cocked an eye at Warren, who quickly assured him that they would be delighted.

Before she could protest, Sloan had eased his tall frame on to the banquette beside her, leaving Warren to seat Ariel on the chair next to him, a task he seemed most eager to perform, Sarah thought drily.

Sloan made the introductions and beckoned for the waitress.

'I really should be going,' muttered Sarah when he asked her what she wanted to drink. She glanced across the table at Ariel, and could see that the gorgeous brunette was annoyed at having to share Sloan with his two co-workers.

'Nonsense,' Sloan said easily. 'Two more of the same here,' he told the waitress, then asked Ariel what she would have.

She really was beautiful, Sarah had to admit, watching her as the discussion about the drinks went on. Her make-up was subtle and professional, and her black hair shone in graceful wings that framed her pale, delicate features. She was wearing a Nile green silk dress, simple and elegant, that moulded every curve without in the least appearing suggestive or cheap. -

Naturally, Sarah thought, Sloan Sheridan would only condescend to bestow his favours on the highest type of woman. She felt dowdy and rumpled, and Sloan was sitting much too close to her. She tried to edge away from him, but he only spread out more, filling the gap between them, his thighs and hips pressed close against hers in the narrow space.

Even in the coolness of the lounge, she began to perspire from the warmth of his hard lean body next to hers. A few times his leg inadvertently moved slightly against hers, and Sarah didn't at all like the way this made her feel. She was becoming far too aware of him as a man at such close quarters.

They chatted over their drinks for another half hour on neutral subjects, and finally, to Sarah's intense relief, Sloan stood up and said that he and Ariel had to be going.

The party broke up, then, and Sarah hurried off to the train station, refusing Warren's offer of a lift home. The whole thing had been strangely disturbing to her, and she just wanted to get away and put the incident out of her mind.

CHAPTER FOUR

THE next day, Sarah made an extra effort to reaffirm her businesslike image. She wore her severest suit, a brown poplin that was neat and well-fitting, but by no means clinging or suggestive. With it she wore a cream silk shirt that she buttoned firmly to the neck. In the office she clamped her glasses firmly on her nose and refused to remove her jacket, even though by afternoon, the small office was stifling.

Sloan and Warren had been gone again all morning, and when Sloan returned alone after lunch, his tone was even more curt and distant than usual. As he barked brief orders at her, Sarah wondered if last night's encounter in the lounge had upset him.

She didn't see why. What she did on her own time was her business. If she wanted to have a drink with Warren after working hours, it was no concern of Sloan Sheridan's. She glanced at him now, bending over his desk, deep in the Burnside file. While Warren was at the courthouse law library involved in his interminable research of the law pertaining to the Alvarez case, Sloan was spending the afternoon catching up on his other cases.

She really didn't like him, she decided, watching the hard look on his face as he leafed through the papers before him. He's too cold, she thought, too domineering. He was leaning slightly forward, his arms lying on the desk on either side of the open file, frowning in concentration.

At four-thirty he got up from his desk and stood in the doorway looking down at her. She glanced up at him enquiringly through her glasses, unruffled and composed, not a hair out of place. His piercing black eyes were cold and distant.

He handed her a yellow legal pad and she glanced through it. Several sheets were covered with his straight slashing strokes. There were a lot of figures, and she groaned inwardly.

'I'd like to get this typed tonight,' he said in a flat voice.

She nodded briefly, accustomed by now to staying late for him at a moment's notice. She didn't mind. There was nothing waiting for her at home, and she was well paid for overtime work.

She began typing, setting up the long columns of figures that required all her powers of concentration. She worked steadily for almost an hour. The office was empty. Everyone else had gone home, and she was grateful for the relative quiet.

It was a complicated job. Even without interruption she'd be there at least another two hours if Sloan really wanted it finished tonight. She sighed then, when she heard him call to her from his office.

'Come in here a moment.'

She took up her shorthand pad and a pen and went into his office. His head was still bent over the papers on his desk.

'Sit down.'

She did so, wondering what lovely job he had in mind for her next. She was tired and longed to get the Armitage figures typed up so she could go home.

Finally Sloan looked at her. He got up and crossed over to the door, shut it firmly, then came back and sat on the edge of the desk, his arms folded across his chest. He had on the same navy blue suit he had worn yesterday, and Sarah wondered idly as she waited for him to start dictating if he'd spent the night at Ariel Boone's.

'I want to have a talk with you.'

His tone was cold and forbidding. Startled, she sat up straighter in her chair and looked at him. Why, she thought, does he look so angry? She searched her mind for some error she might have committed in her work. She wasn't infallible, she knew, and only hoped it wasn't too serious. From his manner, however, it sounded like it might be a disaster.

'Yes?' she enquired evenly, composing herself. She knew from experience that it was fatal to show any sign of apprehension.

'I don't like the way you're fooling around with Warren Langley,' he announced tersely.

Sarah's mouth dropped open. 'Fooling around?' she asked, unable to believe her ears. 'I don't understand.'

A mocking sneer appeared on his dark features. 'Oh, come now, Mrs Kincaid, don't try that innocent virginal air on me. You know exactly what I mean. Warren's a nice kid, he'll make a good lawyer once he's dry behind the ears. I don't want his career ruined by a sordid affair with a married woman.'

Sarah had recovered from her first shock by now. As soon as she saw what he was driving at, an icy calm descended on her. Really, she thought, this was too much! The hell with him and his rules!

She stood up, put her pad and pen down on the desk and gave him a long icy stare, her fists clenched at her sides, every muscle rigid. She drew a deep breath and plunged ahead.

'But I'm not married,' she said in a patient tone, as if to a child. 'Surely you knew that?'

It was his turn to looked shocked. Sarah almost laughed aloud. Now that she had decided to burn her bridges, it gave her intense pleasure to see Sloan Sheridan's controlled façade falter.

However, he hadn't risen to his position of prominence as a trial lawyer for nothing. He swiftly recovered himself and narrowed his eyes at her.

'Then you deceived me,' he accused sternly. 'You told me you were married when I hired you. You knew my rule against hiring single women.'

'I *was* married when you hired me,' she replied evenly. 'My husband died shortly after I came here. It was in all the newspapers, and I'm sure the topic of office gossip for quite a while.'

'You know I never listen to office gossip, and if it was in the paper, I either didn't read it or didn't connect it with my own secretary.'

He made it sound as though that was her fault. Nice try, she thought, still standing her ground. Even though he covered it well, she could see that he was still stunned by the news of her single status. She felt an intense satisfaction at his discomfiture.

There was a long silence, then. Sarah was determined not to budge an inch, and Sloan seemed deep in thought, staring pensively down at the brown carpet.

Finally he cocked his head slightly to one side and gave her an appraising look. 'So you're not married,' he said softly.

'No,' she snapped, 'I'm not.' She began to feel uncomfortable under his cool calculating gaze. Her heart began to pound erratically and it was with an effort that she made her voice steady. 'So you needn't worry about Warren's reputation.'

She had no intention of telling him that

she had no interest in Warren Langley of a personal nature. Let him stew a little!

His eyes narrowed at her. 'I should fire you,' he muttered.

'Very well,' she said calmly. 'I'll go collect my things,' and she started towards the door.

She had to pass by him to get there. Out of the corner of her eye, she saw him straighten up, then felt a strong merciless grip clamp down on her upper arm. Startled, she turned to him, glaring, ready to do battle, but the look in those dark eyes frightened her. His grip bit painfully into the soft skin of her arm, even through her suit jacket, and she began to worry that he might really hurt her. He seemed barely able to contain some intense emotion. He reached up with his free hand and pulled her glasses roughly off her nose, flinging them carelessly down on the desk.

'Damn it,' he muttered, his face only inches away from hers, 'I'm going to break through that icy reserve of yours if it kills us both!'

They were so close now that she could feel his breath on her face, smell the distinctive masculine scent of tobacco and faint aftershave, see the way his fine nostrils flared, the little pulse beating at his jawline, and she knew he was either going to kiss her or hit her.

At this point she didn't really care which. Whether he chose to use violence or his own seductive power, she knew she was no match for him, physically or otherwise. She closed her eyes and waited.

His mouth came down hard on hers at first, punishing, grinding, but then, when she made no attempt to struggle or resist, forcing herself to remain impassive under the plundering onslaught, his lips gentled. His hand released its vicelike grip on her arm and slid up over her shoulder and around to the back of her neck.

In spite of all her resolution, Sarah felt herself responding to him. She couldn't help herself. Sloan was undoing her hair now, dropping the pins heedlessly on the

carpet, running his hands through the heavy
honey-gold mass as it fell free.

He tore his mouth from hers and, cupping
her face in his large strong hands, gazed
deeply down into her eyes. Sarah saw a look
there she had never seen before, overpowering in its intensity, the black pupils
dilated. His cruel lips were soft now,
seductively curved.

'You're so beautiful,' he murmured softly,
moving his long fingers over her cheekbones,
her nose, her chin. 'So remote, so cool.
God, you've been driving me wild! And all
along I thought you were married!'

'Sloan . . .' she managed to choke out. 'I
don't think . . .'

His mouth was on hers again, cutting off
her words. His kiss took her breath away.
His arms came around her, under the jacket
of her suit, his hands sliding sensuously
over the silky material of her blouse.

She shuddered with sheer delight, as the
long lean body pressed up against her and,
wanting to draw him even closer, raised her

arms up around his neck. As she ran her fingers into the thick coarse hair, her lips parted and when his kiss deepened she knew she was lost.

It had been years since a man had held her like this, and no man, not even Derek at the height of her infatuation for him, had been able to evoke such a heady, mindless response from her. Every ounce of sleeping passion under her cool exterior had been awakened and was crying out for release.

His rough cheek was on hers now, his lips at her ear, his heavy breath sending almost painful sensations rippling through her body. One hand was at her throat, sliding back and forth over the skin of her neck, then moving slowly downward to rest possessively on her breast.

She could feel his breath quicken to match her own as the hand slid tantalisingly over the soft full mound.

'God,' he breathed in her ear, 'I've wanted to do this ever since the Christmas party, when I saw the beautiful desirable woman under that prim act you put on!'

He drew back from her a little, and she ran her hands down over his chest, to settle at his waistline. She couldn't speak. He looked into her eyes.

'I want you, Sarah,' he breathed. 'I've got to have you. I want to undress you. I want to make love to you.' His hand moved now to the top button of her blouse, deftly freeing it. 'You want me, too,' he said, as his hand slid down her breast to the next button. 'You know you do.'

'Ah, Sloan,' she sighed, arching towards him, longing to feel those strong hands on her bare flesh. She raised her hands to his face, cupping it, running her fingers over the flat planes, the high cheekbones, the strong jaw and chin.

Just then the telephone on his desk shrilled loudly. Sarah jumped, but Sloan held her fast. 'Ignore it,' he murmured as his hand slipped inside her blouse at last.

But the spell was broken. The phone kept

ringing, and Sarah drew back from him abruptly. What had she done? She clutched her blouse together and stared at him. This was Sloan Sheridan, her boss—the man whose cast-offs she had had to comfort so many times in the past five years.

The phone finally stopped ringing. With a little cry, Sarah turned and ran from the room. He came striding after her, standing over her as she reached down to retrieve her purse.

'Sarah,' he began when she straightened up. He put a hand on her arm.

'No,' she cried, horrified. 'Don't touch me!'

She slid past him and started running down the hall, her hair streaming out behind her, frantically buttoning up her blouse as she ran. He called to her once more before she turned the corner at the end of the corridor, but she never looked back, and he didn't come after her.

It was dark by the time Sarah got home that

night, and a blanket of fog had drifted in over the Bay. She was still trembling when she let herself in the door of her house, both from the cold mist and her own turbulent emotions. The minute she walked inside, the telephone started ringing. She didn't answer it. She didn't want to talk to anyone, and she ran into the kitchen to pull the plug so she wouldn't have to listen to the insistent ringing.

She felt so violated, she thought, shivering as she ran a bath and got out of her clothes. All the defences she had built so carefully and painfully over the past five years had crumbled in an instant. She had vowed over and over never to fall into that kind of trap with that kind of man ever again, and at the first touch of his kiss, his hands, she had stepped right into it.

Sloan Sheridan was Derek Kincaid all over again, she thought, as she scrubbed viciously at her body in the bath. Only more so. More clever, more compelling, more unscrupulous. And more sexually attractive and determined to get his own way no matter who was hurt. Far, far more dangerous, too.

Like Derek, he had only one thing on his mind where women were concerned—his own pleasure, the thrill of conquest. Never mind the poor gullible female who wanted to believe their promises, their lies.

As she dried herself, she started shivering again, remembering with almost physical pain how close she had come tonight with Sloan. Thank God for the persistent Mrs Armitage, or whoever had called on the telephone at just that instant.

By the time she had had a bowl of soup and a cup of coffee, she was calmer. Nothing irrevocable actually had happened, she thought gratefully, but on one thing her mind was firmly made up. She would never go back to work for Sloan Sheridan now that she had undeniable proof of his intentions and of her own weakness.

Before she went to bed that night she typed out a carefully worded, impersonal letter of resignation, addressed to Sloan, saying only that she was quitting her job for personal reasons. She knew she was leaving him in the lurch professionally, and she was sincerely sorry about that. But after all, she thought, he was the one who made the rule about married secretaries. He was the one who had threatened to fire her when she first realised she no longer had a husband.

It didn't matter anyway. Not for worlds would she ever risk facing him again.

By the next morning, after a good night's sleep, she began to have second thoughts about her decision. She wondered if perhaps she hadn't overreacted to the highly-charged encounter with Sloan last night. After all, she thought as she stood at the kitchen counter in her bathrobe drinking a glass of orange juice, it was only a kiss.

Well, she thought, colouring, a little more than a kiss. She really liked her job, and perhaps if she put it to Sloan firmly that there must never be a repetition of what happened last night, they could still work together. She knew how much he valued her services and he probably didn't want an involvement any more than she did.

Thinking it over more calmly now in the light of day, she wondered what in the world had got into him last night. It was so out of character for him to make a pass at his secretary, in direct contradiction to all the rules *he* had laid down.

It must have been the shock of discovering she wasn't married after all, she decided, as she made the coffee and put bread in the toaster. He had mentioned the Christmas party last night, said he'd first really noticed her as a woman then. She thought he had been giving her strange looks ever since, and his violent objection to her friendship with Warren Langley made more sense if it meant Sloan was jealous of him.

She had to laugh aloud at that thought. Sloan Sheridan jealous? Never. No, she mused, sipping the strong hot coffee, the kiss meant nothing to him. Perhaps she could continue working for him after all if they were both careful. Sex was only a game to him anyway, and his work came before everything else.

Then she remembered the feel of his mouth on hers, the heady scent of him, the way his hands had moved over her, the strong lean body pressing on hers, and her hand began to tremble so she had to set her cup down rattling on to the saucer.

It might have meant nothing to him, she thought starkly, but it had shattered her. With all his other women to choose from for his sexual adventures, he didn't need her. He'd be quite capable of resuming their old relationship for the sake of his law practice. But would she? She sighed deeply, totally confused.

She needed time to think, she decided. She glanced at the clock. It was two minutes to nine. Nancy, the receptionist, went on duty at eight-thirty.

Sarah plugged the phone on the kitchen counter back in and rang the office number.

'Sheridan, Wright and Brubaker, good morning,' came Nancy's pleasant voice.

'Good morning, Nancy, it's me—Sarah. I won't be in today. I'm not feeling well.'

She heard Nancy gasp. 'I can't believe it! You've never taken a day's sick leave since you've been here. Do you want to talk to Sloan?'

'No,' Sarah replied hurriedly. 'You tell him.'

After she had hung up, she wondered if she had done the right thing. Surely Sloan would realise just what an impact he'd made on her last night if she didn't show up today for work? Yet she knew she would never have been able to go into the office today and face him, work with him, as though nothing had happened. It was too soon.

Besides, she thought defiantly, Nancy was right. I never have taken a day's sick leave since I started. She enjoyed almost perfect health, and the few times she'd felt a cold or 'flu coming on there always seemed to be too much for her to do at the office to stay at home.

The phone started ringing. It was probably Sloan. She thought guiltily about Mrs Armitage's quarterly report, still lying on her desk untyped. 'That's too bad,' she said aloud. There were other typists in the office. Let them decipher Sloan's slashing scrawls!

She reached over and pulled the plug on the phone.

By noon the fog had cleared, and the April sun shone warmly enough for Sarah to work out in the garden cleaning up the debris of winter and deciding what annuals she wanted to set out.

She worked through the afternoon quite happily, and by the time she sun started to go down, around six o'clock, the episode with Sloan seemed like a dream. The day had passed so pleasantly that she vowed to take more time off from work.

She had allowed herself to become nothing but a slave to Sloan Sheridan and his law practice over the past five years. It was time she began thinking about getting on with her own life, she decided. At twenty-six she was hardly senile. Maybe she'd take some evening classes at the University.

She thought about her letter of resignation still lying unmailed on her desk. She still hadn't made up her mind whether to send it or not.

That evening after supper, she decided on an impulse to call her sister Margaret in Santa Barbara. They hadn't had a real visit since Christmas, merely exchanged a few newsy letters. After that one conversation at their parents' house, when Margaret had announced that she was leaving Robert, she had clammed up and refused to discuss it.

Sarah wondered now what Margaret's intentions were. Also, she realised, as she plugged in the telephone and dialled Margaret's number, she just wanted to talk to her sister.

'Hello,' came Margaret's voice.

'It's Sarah, Margaret. How are you?'

'Sarah?' came the bewildered voice. 'Is something wrong?'

'No, silly!' Sarah laughed. 'I just wanted to talk to you—it's been a while. How are things?'

There was a short silence on the other end. Then, 'What things?' came the curt reply.

'Oh, you know, the usual—Robert, Billy,' Sarah said lightly. 'After all, we are related.'

She heard Margaret sigh heavily. 'Yes, I know what you mean. Nothing's been decided.' She laughed shortly. 'It seems you were right about—things. There was nothing between Robert and his little widow. Nothing physical, that is.'

'Meaning?' Sarah asked.

'Meaning that they aren't having an affair, that Robert is still technically faithful to me, but . . .'

'But what?' Sarah prompted.

'I can't really go into it now, Sarah. He's still seeing her—says it's professional concern, whatever that means. I don't like it, and he knows it, but what can I do?'

It wasn't like the supremely self-confident Margaret to admit defeat. 'Just what you're doing, I guess. Hang in there.'

'Oh, I intend to—for now. Well, enough of that.' Margaret's voice took on a brisk tone. 'What's new with you?'

'I'm thinking about quitting my job,' Sarah replied slowly.

She heard Margaret draw in her breath sharply. 'I don't believe it! Whatever for? I thought you loved it.'

'I did. I do.' Her voice faltered. 'It's just that . . .'

'Don't tell me you've fallen for him, too,' said Margaret.

'Of course not,' Sarah snapped. 'It's just that I think I need a change. Five years is a long time to put up with the kind of demands Sloan Sheridan makes on a secretary. There are other things in life besides a job, after all.'

'I've been trying to tell you that ever

since Derek was killed,' Margaret reminded her drily. 'I'm glad to hear you finally agree.'

'Then you think I should quit?'

'I didn't say that. You're not the type to make snap decisions—not like me,' her sister added on a wry note. 'I'd give it a little more thought if I were you.'

'Maybe you're right. I'll think about it. Give my nephew a big kiss and Robert my love.'

They said goodbye, then, and hung up. While Sarah still had her hand on the receiver, deep in thought over the conversation with her sister, the telephone rang shrilly. Absently she picked it up.

'Hello.'

'How are you feeling?' came a curt familiar voice.

Sarah's heart started pounding, and her knees felt weak. She lowered herself into a nearby chair and put a hand over her forehead.

'Much better,' she said at last in a low voice.

'That's good. When Nancy told me you were off sick, I could hardly believe my ears. It's the first time, isn't it?'

'Yes, it is,' she replied. His voice was so brisk and businesslike, she thought, as if nothing had happened. She didn't know whether to be glad or sorry.

'Listen,' he went on. 'I hope you'll be well enough to come in Monday. I'm in a hell of a mess down here. I can't find anything, and these girls can't seem to be able to read plain English or type a single paragraph without a dozen errors. I don't know why we hire such incompetents!'

Plain English, Sarah thought, raising her eyes in supplication. Is that what he thought that handwriting of his was? It had taken her weeks to learn to decipher those bold upright strokes.

'Well?' His voice was impatient. 'Will you be here on Monday or not? If not, I might as well get sick, too.'

She couldn't answer. She knew she should say something, but she still couldn't make up her mind just what it should be. He sounded as though he had forgotten all about that highly-charged episode in his office last night. Was that perhaps the best way to handle it? Wasn't that what she wanted?

Then she knew she couldn't just drop it. If she was going to continue to work for him, it must never happen again. He was still waiting for her reply.

'Sloan,' she said, 'I've been thinking about leaving, looking for another job.'

There was a short silence. Then, 'Look, Sarah,' he said in a low voice, 'about what happened last night. I won't go into any lengthy explanations, except to apologise and promise you it won't happen again.'

Sloan Sheridan! Sarah thought in amazement. Apologising! He must really want her back desperately.

'What about your rule?' she asked.

'What rule?'

She sighed. What convenient memories some men had! 'Your rule about not hiring single secretaries. You did say last night you ought to fire me for *deceiving* you. Which I didn't, by the way,' she couldn't resist adding.

'Yes, well, I realise now you didn't deliberately deceive me. And since you were married when I hired you, the rule remains inviolate.'

Ah, to have a lawyer's mentality! she thought. They could twist everything around to suit their purposes.

'Well,' she said slowly, 'if you promise. No more . . . er . . .' She didn't know quite how to phrase it.

'Passes?' he broke in. 'Hanky-panky?' He chuckled deep in his throat. 'I promise,' he said firmly. 'Absolutely none.'

Sarah couldn't help feeling a little stung. 'You sound very sure of yourself,' she commented tartly.

'Oh, I am, I am,' he drawled. 'There are plenty of women more receptive to my— er—advances than you seem to be, but a good secretary is a pearl beyond price.

That's settled, then? You'll be in on Monday?'

'I'll see how I feel,' she said, and hung up.

That arrogant, conceited swine! she thought, seething. I've got a good notion to stay out sick another week. Serve him right! Plenty of girls more receptive to his advances, indeed!

Still, she thought, when she calmed down, he was right. There seemed to be a surfeit of women anxious to fall into Sloan Sheridan's arms. And at least he didn't put her in that category, even after the way she had responded to him last night.

Her face burned as she recalled that mindless response. How could he have missed it? He didn't, she realised, as she began clearing off her dinner dishes. He's just made up his mind to pretend it never happened. If he can do it, so can I, she promised herself.

CHAPTER FIVE

On Monday morning, all Sarah's apprehensions vanished the moment she walked into her office and saw Sloan at her desk frantically searching through the disorderly pile of papers and files. She sighed when she saw her neat filing system now in total disarray.

He looked up at her gloomily. 'Where did you put the Burnside file?' he asked accusingly.

Situation normal, she thought, as she calmly walked around her desk. He knew quite well he was the last one to have the file. She reached down under her typewriter to tuck her handbag on the shelf underneath, then straightened up and stood beside him. She looked down at her cluttered desk, appalled at the havoc wreaked there in one day's absence.

She glanced up at him, and her heart began to beat a little faster at the sight of those strong features, his mouth set grimly now in a firm line. He made an impatient gesture with his hand.

'I can't find anything,' he complained.

Her heart slowed its pace when she saw that it was the same old Sloan, and she smiled to herself. Really, he was an exasperating man! Yet there was something about his helplessness that made him strangely endearing. He stood beside her now like a small boy who couldn't find his favourite baseball glove.

Without a word, she walked into his office. She turned over the stacks of files on his desk, then glanced through those on the credenza behind it, then the pile on the floor. She took out a thick manila folder near the bottom and placed it on his desk.

Then she walked back into her own office. 'It was on the floor,' she remarked mildly. 'You must have overlooked it.'

Sloan merely grunted and strode past her to his desk. Soon he was deeply immersed in the newly resurrected file, and Sarah turned to face the unpleasant task of straightening out the mess on her desk.

It took her all day to attain some semblance of order out of the chaos and to finish the work that had piled up on Friday. She worked through her lunch hour, eating her sandwich at her desk, and by five o'clock she had even made some inroads into the additional work Sloan had given her to do during the day.

Still, there was a lot to be done, and she didn't look forward to facing a mountain of unfinished work tomorrow. She had just decided to stay over another hour or so to get her desk cleared, when Sloan spoke to her from his office.

'It's five o'clock.'

'I know that,' she replied, opening the Armitage file. 'I just want to finish up this quarterly report before I go.'

'No, it's five o'clock. Go home. If you

have too much work to do for a normal working day, I'll see about getting you some help.'

I must be dreaming, she thought. She gave him a searching look, but he was bent over his desk, scribbling furiously on a legal pad. Sarah continued to stare, unspeaking, wondering what to make of this sudden concern for her welfare.

Then he glanced at her, and the corners of his mouth quirked a little. 'You're no good to me sick, you know. Maybe I've been piling the work on a little thick, taking too much for granted.'

'That's not true,' she said in a low voice. 'I can handle anything you can dish out, and you know it.'

For a moment, a wicked gleam appeared in the near-black eyes and the heavy eyebrows were raised in a question. Sarah felt the blood rush to her face as the implications of her statement and his reaction dawned on her. Well, she amended to herself, almost everything.

Abruptly, he turned back to his work. 'We'll see,' he muttered. 'But go on home now. I'll be over in Marin County at a deposition in the Alvarez case all day tomorrow, and you'll have time to catch up then.'

'All right, then,' Sarah said stiffly. She reached down to get her bag and stood up to go. 'Goodnight.'

During the next few months, Sarah was so busy she didn't have time to think of Sloan in any way except as a demanding boss she had to run to keep up with. That first day back had been mildly disturbing, but it had set the right tone for their working relationship, and in time she had almost forgotten that this remote, impersonal man had once held her in his arms and kissed her.

Almost, but not quite. At odd times the incident would recur in her mind. It was June now, and the streets and trains and shops of San Francisco seemed to be filled with lovers. Every time she caught sight of a couple locked in passionate embrace in the most unlikely places, she would remember, and experience a little glow, a bittersweet ache.

In early May she had sent the standard card along with two dozen red roses to Ariel Boone, and wondered who would be next on her boss's list of conquests. So far, office gossip had not come up with a replacement for the glamorous model, and there was even some speculation in the coffee room that the great man had turned celibate.

Sarah had to laugh when she heard that rumour. Sooner the Golden Gate Bridge would collapse into the sea than Sloan Sheridan give up women, and she congratulated herself on her own narrow escape.

On a Wednesday evening in mid-June, Sloan called her at home after dinner. She had been out in the garden watering after a long dry spell and had to stop to wipe her feet and dry her hands before running into the kitchen to answer the phone.

'I'm coming, I'm coming!' she called as the phone shrilled insistently. She was out of breath by the time she lifted the receiver, and when she heard Sloan's voice on the other end, her heartbeat accelerated even faster. In five years, he had probably called her at home only half a dozen times, and it never failed to give her an odd, unsettling feeling of intimacy when he did, even though it was always on business.

'I've got to go to Santa Barbara first thing in the morning for a deposition in the Alvarez case,' he stated brusquely with no preamble. 'It's an important witness—Mrs Layton's ex-husband. One of several,' he added drily.

'I see,' Sarah murmured absently, and automatically reached for the pad and pencil she always kept handy by the telephone. He would have instructions for her, she knew, so she could deal with his other cases in his absence.

'I want you to go with me,' he went on in a matter-of-fact tone, and the point of her pencil broke from the sudden pressure of her muscles tensing.

It wasn't unheard-of for her to go on business trips with him, but it was rare, and certainly not since that night in April when their relationship had suddenly become so disturbing. Nothing at all of a personal nature had passed between them since then, but the thought of going on a trip with him made Sarah very wary.

'We'll drive down,' Sloan was saying. His tone was curt and businesslike. 'I'd take Langley, but he's up to his ears in research and I need him to go to court tomorrow on the Burnside motion.'

She couldn't speak. She just stood there, leaning over the kitchen counter, the broken pencil still clutched in her hand.

'Kincaid, are you there?' He sounded annoyed.

'Er . . . yes, I'm here.' She paused. 'Why do you need me?' she asked in a small voice. 'Won't you have a court reporter?'

'Damn it, don't argue with me!' he

barked. 'I need you because this is a crucial witness, and I want you to take notes so I can concentrate on my questions. Is that okay?'

Her heart sank. She'd have to go. She thought it over. Perhaps she was being foolish. She remembered his words about a good secretary being a pearl beyond price. He didn't want a personal involvement any more than she did.

'What time do you want to leave?' she asked in a firmer tone.

'I'll pick you up at seven. We can hit the freeway early and get to Santa Barbara by noon. The deposition will run through the next morning if I get what I want from this guy, so be prepared to spend the night.'

She could stay with Margaret, she thought, and her spirits rose.

She was waiting for Sloan on the front porch of her house promptly at seven o'clock the next morning, her overnight case packed. It was a beautiful day, sunny and warm and not a trace of fog. Sarah wore an uncrushable off-white polyester suit for the ride down, and had packed a fresh blouse for the next day, underwear and night clothes.

Margaret had been delighted when she'd called last night to see if it would be convenient for her to stay, and Sarah looked forward to a good visit with her sister and her family.

Sloan's sleek, dark Mercedes appeared at the kerb shortly after seven. Sarah picked up her light suitcase and walked quickly down the path to the car so that he wouldn't have to get out, but by the time she got there he was standing on the sidewalk reaching for her bag.

He wore well-fitting cocoa brown trousers, a subdued tie and a lightweight fawn jacket. His crisp white shirt gleamed against the dark tan of his face, and Sarah thought he looked dazzling standing there so tall next to the luxurious car.

'That's what I like,' he remarked as he

stowed her bag in the back seat, 'a prompt woman.'

He stood smiling down at her. Sarah was disconcerted. This pleasant, attractive man was a different Sloan Sheridan from the cold, detached machine she was used to dealing with in the office. She had a sudden insane impulse to take the pins out of her hair, remove her glasses and pretend she was a woman instead of an efficient secretary.

She got inside the car and watched him covertly as he strode around the front to the driver's side. She saw him pause, glance up at the sky, then remove his jacket. He slid in beside her and leaned over to drape the jacket neatly on the back seat. Then he took off his tie and rolled up the sleeves of his shirt to just below his elbows.

He gave her a quick glance. 'It's going to be warm going down through the San Joaquin Valley,' he said, 'and I detest air-conditioning. You'd better take your jacket off.'

Sarah by now was intensely aware of the sheer animal magnetism of the man, and this made her uncomfortable. She had never seen him like this before, his collar unbuttoned to reveal the smooth base of his throat, the strong forearms covered with fine silky black hair, the muscles rippling as he grasped the steering wheel and started the car. Above all, the pleasant friendly manner.

Apprehension began to gnaw at her as she slipped off her jacket and placed it demurely over her shoulders. She thought she detected the dark eyes flashing briefly at her in amusement as he pulled away from the kerb, and she began to feel silly.

The drive down through the sprawling orchards and truck farms of the San Joaquin Valley was a hot one, but pleasant, and gradually Sarah's nervousness vanished as Sloan filled her in on the witness he was to depose that afternoon and what he wanted her to do.

From time to time she couldn't help

noticing how the breeze through the open window blew about his thick black hair. She'd never seen him looking in the least rumpled before, and the untidy hair softened his stern features, giving him a boyish look.

As the sun rose higher in the sky, he began to squint against it, deepening the creases at the corners of his eyes, and he asked her to reach in the glove compartment of the car to get his sunglasses.

When she pressed the button, however, nothing happened. 'It's stuck,' she said, trying again.

'You have to use a little muscle,' he said, and his arm shot in front of her, brushing against her as he gave it a harder push with his thumb.

Bending over to hide the confusion his touch created in her, Sarah fumbled inside the compartment until she found a glasses case. She took it out and handed it to him, but not before she had seen, by the inner light, a distinctly feminine compact and scarf. She slammed the door shut, vaguely disturbed by what she had seen. It was none of her business, she told herself firmly, but still she couldn't shake off a feeling of annoyance.

They left the freeway and stopped for a quick lunch on the outskirts of Santa Barbara around noon. Nearer the ocean now, the weather had cooled considerably, and Sloan put his jacket and tie back on again before getting into the car when they left the restaurant.

The deposition was to be held at the offices of the witness's attorney, who was an old friend and classmate of Sloan's, and as they drove there after lunch, Sarah was reminded of how much she liked the small city, with its quiet, opulent atmosphere, its narrow streets heavily shaded by giant jacarandas, live oak, eucalyptus and pepper trees, the quaint Spanish architecture with its red tile roofs and pastel stucco buildings.

Sloan's lawyer friend, David Hardy, was a jovial man with the beginning of a spare tyre around the middle and thinning fair hair.

He was courteous to Sarah, offering her the firm's pleasant powder room to freshen up in after the long drive, but after one glance at her prim suit, glasses and no-nonsense hairstyle, he gave her a cool glance of dismissal that Sarah found highly amusing.

The afternoon passed quickly. The witness, Mrs Layton's second husband out of four, and Martha's father, was co-operative to the point of condemning both the girl and her mother as self-seeking liars, and Sarah knew the trip had been well worthwhile.

Although she was kept busy taking notes, she enjoyed watching Sloan in action, the knack he had of leading his witness gradually, but inexorably, to just the point he wanted him to make. His tone was always reasonable, reassuring, and only became curt and peremptory when he sensed the witness straying from the point he wanted to make into personal side issues.

They broke at five o'clock and were to continue the following morning. Deep in conversation, the three men left the pleasant small conference room where the deposition was held, and Sarah stood up gratefully, stretching to get the kinks out of her back. Then she began to gather her things together and collect Sloan's notes. The court reporter, a plump young woman with dark hair and heavy make-up, was still sitting at the table watching her.

'That boss of yours is quite a lawyer,' the girl remarked as she put her dictating machine together. She grinned. 'And quite a hunk of man, too, I might add! I'll bet he's murder in a courtroom—and elsewhere!'

Sarah murmured a noncommittal reply, and was glad to see Sloan appear in the doorway. She didn't like to discuss her boss with anyone. Even the most innocent remarks could be misinterpreted to work against him professionally. With one frankly appreciative glance, the reporter brushed past him. Sloan didn't even glance at her. Poor girl, Sarah thought, there's a long line ahead of you. And thank God I'm not in it, she added fervently to herself.

'Come on, Kincaid,' Sloan said curtly, beckoning to her. 'I'll take you to your sister's.'

It had been a long day for him, Sarah thought. He looked tired. She knew enough by now, however, not to mention that fact. She'd had her head bitten off once for that.

She directed him to her sister's house, a pleasant white stucco rambler set high on a bluff overlooking the crowded harbour below. Santa Barbara was not a commercial port, but its many wealthy residents kept the sheltered bay jammed with pleasure boats of every description.

'Can you mangage all right on your own?' Sloan asked as she got out of the car.

'Certainly,' she replied, reaching into the back seat for her overnight case. She was looking forward to a quiet evening with her sister and her family.

'Good. I'll pick you up at eight, then.'

Sarah stood on the sidewalk and stared down at him. He was leaning across the passenger seat, his head at the window.

'Pick me up?' she stammered. 'What for?' On their previous trips out of town he had always had his own evening social engagements, leaving her free to do as she pleased.

'We're going out to dinner with Dave Hardy and Jack Layton,' he explained impatiently.

'But . . .' she began.

He frowned. 'Don't argue, Kincaid. Just be ready at eight.' He looked her up and down appraisingly, insolently. 'And for God's sake, wear something that doesn't make you look like a middle-aged spinster!'

She opened her mouth to protest, but he frowned fiercely, silencing her.

'Don't look so nervous, Kincaid,' he said impatiently. 'I'm not going to attack you, for God's sake. I don't want an involvement any more than you do.'

With that he drove off, leaving Sarah on the sidewalk, her suitcase at her feet, almost spluttering with annoyance. Who does he think he is? she asked herself angrily. A middle-aged spinster, indeed! Does he think he owns me?

Well, she thought as she walked up to the front door and pressed the bell, he can think again. I just won't go. Surely, with a little black book the size of his, there must be someone in Santa Barbara ready to go out to dinner with him at a moment's notice.

'Is that scowl meant for me or for life in general?' came her sister's voice from the open door. 'You look like a process server or a bill collector!'

Sarah smiled at her and kissed her affectionately. 'Sorry, Margaret, it's been a long day.'

The house was cool and quiet, a large pleasant home, with tiled floors, Spanish rugs, adobe walls and dark woodwork. Margaret explained that Robert and Billy had gone for a walk on the beach.

'Why the disguise?' she asked as they walked down a wide corridor to the bedroom Sarah was to occupy.

Sarah set her suitcase down on the bed

and took off her glasses. 'You mean these?' she asked with a grin.

Margaret nodded. '*And* the disgusting hairstyle. *And* the shapeless suit.'

'Actually, you're right. It is a disguise—my professional image.'

'Well, please drop it while you're here. I think I might get sick!'

A wicked idea flashed into Sarah's mind. 'I might just do that tonight,' she said slowly, 'if you can lend me a dress.'

She explained about the dinner arrangements Sloan had made with David Hardy and his parting comment about her looks. The sisters were about the same size, and Margaret entered into the idea with great glee. Their colouring was different, but Sarah knew that out of Margaret's vast wardrobe they should be able to come up with something that wouldn't overwhelm her. Margaret's taste ran to flamboyance, with vibrant colours and plunging necklines.

They spent half an hour arguing over the right selection. Sarah had rejected one gorgeous, but too exotic, dress after another, as too bright or too provocative.

'It's all right for you,' she said at last, flopping down on Margaret's bed. 'You're a safely married woman. I can't go to a business dinner looking like a seductress on the prowl. I want to teach Sloan a lesson, but there are limits!'

'Well, you've *been* married,' Margaret countered in disgust. 'You're not exactly a blushing virgin, and surely with your looks you haven't been celibate since Derek died.' Her eyes widened at the red flush that crept over Sarah's face. 'Have you?' she probed. Sarah averted her eyes. 'Oh, my God,' Margaret breathed, 'I don't believe it!'

'Now, Margaret,' Sarah said in a warning tone, 'don't start on that. Let me run my life my way.'

'All right, all right, little sister, don't get frosty.' Margaret poked around in the back of the closet. 'Say,' came her muffled voice, 'this might be just the thing.'

She emerged holding up a pale, icy green

dress, very simple, with a low rounded neckline and cap sleeves. It was loosely gathered at the waistline with a narrow tie belt.

'*Voilà!*' she cried. 'Just the thing! Demure yet elegant. Sexy yet virginal. I'll help you with your make-up and hair after you've showered. What do you think? I have some white high-heeled sandals that will be perfect with it.'

Sarah loved the dress. Margaret was right—it was a perfect compromise between the low-key image she preferred and the more feminine one Sloan seemed to expect.

Robert and Billy came bursting into the house just then, and Sarah had about an hour to visit with them over drinks. She was fond of her staid, rather pompous brother-in-law. He was the perfect foil for Margaret's scatterbrained and impulsive vivacity.

She watched them carefully as they all sat chatting comfortably together. They had taken their drinks outside on the tiled loggia, covered with open lathwork and hung with bright red bougainvillea. Everything seemed to be normal. She hoped they had been able to work out their problems, and promised herself she would broach the subject with Margaret as soon as they had some time alone.

At seven o'clock, while the others had their dinner, Sarah showered and washed her hair. She had put on her underthings and was sitting at the dressing table blowdrying her hair when Margaret returned. Their eyes met in the mirror.

'Sorry, darling,' Margaret drawled, 'but demure as that little dress is, I think you'll find it won't take a bra and slip. Not unless you want to be pushing straps under those little sleeves all evening.'

'Then I'll just have to wear my suit,' Sarah said firmly. 'I am not—definitely, positively not—going out to dinner with Sloan Sheridan without underwear on.'

'Why not?' Margaret was incredulous. 'It's done all the time, now.'

'Wait until you meet him,' Sarah said drily. 'It would be like offering myself on a plate to a piranha!'

In the end they settled on a bra-slip that Margaret had tucked away in a drawer, and pinned the narrow straps securely under the little sleeves. Sarah insisted on a bare minimum of make-up, but Margaret did wonders with her heavy mane of dark gold hair, turning the ends under so that it fell just to her shoulders.

At eight o'clock on the dot, the doorbell rang, and for one heart-stopping second Sarah knew she couldn't go through with it.

'Well?' said Margaret. 'Are you going to let him in or shall I?'

The moment of panic passed. It was a business meeting, after all, and although she knew she looked her best, there was nothing provocative about her appearance.

She stood up. 'I'd better do it. He likes promptness.'

When she opened the front door and saw Sloan standing there, breathtakingly handsome in white dinner jacket and black tie, she was too overwhelmed with her own reaction to his impressive good looks to care whether or not he noticed the transformation in her.

They stared openly at each other for a fraction of a second, then, recovering herself, Sarah turned and led him into the large living room.

'I'd like you to meet my sister and brother-in-law,' she said.

After the introductions had been made, the two men chatted for a moment while Margaret and Sarah went down to the bedroom to get a purse and wrap.

'So that's Sloan Sheridan!' Margaret breathed appreciatively as she handed Sarah a lacy white stole. 'I can see now why you insisted on wearing that slip. Wow!'

'I thought you would,' Sarah murmured drily.

Margaret was silent for a moment, looking at Sarah in an odd way, her head cocked to one side. Finally she spoke.

'It won't hurt you to sleep with the guy,' she said slowly, 'but for God's sake, don't fall in love with him.'

Sarah laughed shortly. 'I have no intention of doing either,' she said firmly. 'Our relationship is purely professional, and we both want to keep it that way.'

'Oh, really?' Margaret drawled. 'I saw the way he looked at you—just like a cat about to enjoy its dinner!'

'I'm sure you're mistaken,' Sarah retorted. 'I'd better go. He doesn't like to be kept waiting.'

During the short drive to the restaurant, neither of them spoke until they were almost there. When Sloan had opened the car door for her at the kerb in front of her sister's house, he had lightly taken her by the arm, then quickly drawn his hand away. After that, conversation didn't seem possible. His touch on her bare arm had sent a ripple through her like a charge of electricity, and during the drive she was so intensely aware of him, sitting only inches away from her, his eyes fixed broodingly on the road ahead, that she couldn't utter a word.

Eventually, as they slid into the parking lot of the restaurant, Sarah pulled herself together. After all, it was a business affair.

'Is there anything special you want me to do tonight?' she asked, thankful that her voice sounded a lot steadier than she felt. She still couldn't face him directly.

She could sense it when he turned to her and gave her a stare. She looked at him. His eyes were mocking, his lips curled in a parody of a smile.

'I can think of a few things,' he drawled, and his eyes flicked briefly down to the low scooped neckline of her dress, then back up to her face.

She flushed uncomfortably under that meaning gaze. How dared he! she thought, wishing with all her heart she'd worn her suit. Without a word she got out of the car and stood waiting for him, every nerve now steeled against him. She only wanted to get through the evening and back to the safety of her prim disguise.

As it turned out, however, she found herself enjoying the evening immensely as it progressed. The other two men, Dave Hardy and Jack Layton, gave her frankly appreciative looks the moment they laid eyes on her in the dim cosy lounge, and she glowed happily under their assiduous attentions.

As they drank their wine and ate their delicious steaks, Sarah flirted outrageously with the other two men, and was intensely gratified to see that Sloan became more silent and brooding as the evening wore on.

She didn't care. Let him sulk, she thought, as she danced with Dave Hardy after dinner. He was the one who had insisted she come to dinner. He was the one who had told her not to show up looking like a middle-aged spinster. And he was the one who had made the suggestive remark out in the parking lot. If her behaviour made him uncomfortable, he had only himself to thank for it. It served him right!

By now, Dave was feeling the effects of the brandy he had downed like water after dinner, and the mild flirting had begun to take an alarmingly serious direction. He held her close, too close, on the crowded dance floor, breathing alcoholically into her face, his eyes glazed, his hands clutching her around the waist.

'You're just like Cinderella,' he babbled happily into her ear. 'When I first saw you today at the office I wrote you off as a prudish icicle.' His hand moved on her back. 'I see now I was wrong,' he went on tipsily. 'You know, I get up to San Francisco often on business. Maybe we could get together, have a little fun.'

Sarah was appalled. She tried to draw away from him, but this only made him hold on to her more tightly. She didn't want to insult her boss's friend, but she found his pawing and suggestive innuendoes more than she could tolerate. A little harmless flirting was one thing, she thought, an outright attempt at seduction quite another.

Just as she had pulled back sharply and was about to tell him what she thought of his proposition in no uncertain terms, she saw Sloan appear behind him, towering over him, cold sober, one hand planted firmly on Dave's shoulder.

'Sorry, Dave,' came the smooth voice. His tone was pleasant, but with an undertone of grim determination. 'It's time I got Mrs Kincaid back to her sister's house. I want to get an early start tomorrow.'

Before she could even say goodnight. Sloan had gripped her firmly by the arm and was propelling her before him off the dance floor and towards the exit. At the door she stopped him.

'My wrap,' she murmured in protest. 'My purse.'

Without a word, he shoved them at her and kept moving out of the door and into the parking lot, pulling her along behind him.

It was dark out by now. Sarah shivered a little in the cool breeze from off the ocean, and draped the white stole around her shoulders.

'Get in,' Sloan barked, opening the passenger door when they arrived at the car. She obeyed, and he slammed the door shut.

She watched him nervously as he strode around in front of the car, tall and forbidding. He seemed so angry. Had she gone too far in her little game? No, she thought defiantly, as he settled himself heavily beside her and started the engine. He had asked for it. The car roared out of the parking lot and out into the street.

He didn't speak all the way to Margaret's, and she steeled herself for an explosion. Let him fire me, she thought to herself. I don't care. I'll stay with Margaret for a while, then fly back when I'm good and ready.

Sloan brought the car to an abrupt halt in front of the house, pulled viciously at the emergency brake, switched off the ignition and turned to her, his jaw set, his eyes piercing in the dim light from the street lamp across the road. She put her hand on the door.

'What time do you want to start in the morning?' she asked in as cool a voice as possible.

'Tomorrow may never come for you,' he bit out at her through clenched teeth.

'What's that supposed to mean?' she asked, turning to him and giving him a level gaze. She would *not* be intimidated.

He was turned towards her, one arm resting over the steering wheel. She could hear his angry breathing as he struggled for control.

'You know damned well what it means,' he grated at her. 'You made a spectacle of yourself tonight at what was supposed to be a business meeting!'

Sarah looked away. 'I don't know what you're talking about,' she said sullenly.

His hand shot out and grabbed her by the chin, forcing her head around to face him.

'Like hell you don't!' he shouted. His gaze flicked her up and down. 'Wearing that provocative dress, flirting with poor Dave Hardy!'

She began to feel really angry now. 'Let go of me,' she snapped. 'What is it with you? You complained this afternoon because I looked so tacky, now you complain when men find me attractive—there's no pleasing you.' Her voice rose, almost out of control. 'I don't know what would satisfy your demanding tastes!'

'I'll show you what would satisfy me,' he grated on a note of triumph, and pulled her roughly to him.

Before she could cry out or pull away, his mouth came down hard on hers. His arms held her so tightly that she could barely breathe, and she could taste the blood in her mouth where the force of his kiss had driven her teeth into the inside of her lips.

She beat feebly on his chest with her fists, every instinct telling her to fight her way to freedom, but the harder she struggled, the more demanding his kiss became and the more firmly he held her.

Her efforts to free herself from that iron grip only seemed to madden him further, yet she was afraid if she relaxed, she would begin to respond to him. Already, as he continued to explore her mouth, she could feel the first faint stirrings of desire. Her mouth slackened, she stopped pounding at him, and her body went limp, her willing lips now moving receptively under his.

He lifted his head then and gazed down into her eyes, a long piercing stare that started out angry, hostile, punishing, but gradually softened to an unmistakable gleam of naked desire.

'Sloan,' she choked out, 'please! This is madness—you know it is. Let me go!'

His hold on her loosened slightly, and she knew in her heart that if she made a determined effort now, he would release her. She hesitated a fraction of a second too long, and when she saw his dark head slowly bending down to her again, she sighed deeply, closed her eyes, and parted her lips to receive him.

His kiss was gentle this time, his mouth mobile and soft, seductively playing with hers until she could hardly bear the sensations rising up in her. She put her arms up and clutched at his head, her hands raking through the thick coarse hair, pulling him closer, so that his mouth was pressed harder against hers.

He put one large hand under her chin, at her throat, forcing her head farther back, kissing her now as she had never been kissed before in her life, reducing her to a mindless response that she would never have dreamed possible.

His hand was splayed out now on the bare flesh of her upper chest, above the low-cut bodice, moving tantalisingly towards her breast, but not quite touching, teasing her until she longed to pull it downward herself. Just as she thought she could bear it no longer, she felt the hand settled firmly on one full, thrusting mound, and she moaned deep in her throat as the sensitive hand moved gently back and fourth across her breasts.

Uncaring now what the outcome might

be, she slipped her hands under Sloan's jacket, pulled his shirt away from his trousers and ran her hands up over the taut hard muscles of his back. She felt him shudder at her touch, then stiffen. His hand stopped its exploration of her breast, and his mouth was suddenly still on hers.

Then, with a deep indrawn breath, he pulled away from her. His hands were on her shoulders now and he looked down at her with a dazed, shocked expresson in the black eyes.

'God, Sarah,' he muttered hoarsely, 'what have I done?'

Immediately, as if a bath of cold water had been thrown over her, Sarah came abruptly to her senses. What had *she* done? she asked herself wildly. With one stricken look, she pulled away from him and moved shakily to press herself up against the car door.

She covered her face with her hands, struggling to collect herself, to find the sheer physical strength to get out of that car and crawl inside the house.

She heard Sloan light a cigarette, smelled the acrid scent of burning tobacco. She still couldn't look at him. Finally, after a long silence that seemed to stretch into eternity, he started speaking to her.

'Sarah, I don't know what to say.' His voice was heavy with self-disgust. 'I promised you no passes, and at the first opportunity I behave like an adolescent schoolboy!' He paused, took a deep breath and then went on. 'It's just that you made me so damned mad tonight, leading Dave Hardy on, watching him touch you when I knew you were off limits for me!'

Sarah pulled her hands from her face and sat staring straight ahead of her, her mind beginning to function at last. She glanced over at him. He was slouched down in his seat, still smoking, his eyes on the ceiling of the car, his head resting on the back of the seat.

He turned towards her and smiled crookedly, almost sadly. 'The long and short of it is that I'm afraid I want you more as a

woman than as a secretary.' He paused.
'And that's saying a lot!'

Sarah felt the first faint stirrings of anger
begin to prickle along her skin. What *he*
wanted, of course, was all that mattered! An
icy calm settled over her. She remembered
Derek. Always *his* needs, *his* desires, *his*
convenience and comfort. Never mind about
what she wanted or needed.

'I see,' she said coolly, giving him an
impassive look, deliberately blank. 'What do
you propose to do about it?'

Sloan raised his eyebrows in faint surprise,
straightened up and leaned over to stub out
his cigarette in the ashtray on the dash.

'First of all,' he said, 'I propose to fire
you.' He looked at her, but she didn't blink
an eye. She intended to quit her job anyway.
'Then,' he went on, 'I propose to take you
to bed as soon as possible.'

Of course, she thought. It was so simple.
'Well, you can think again!' she snapped,
glaring at him now. 'I have no intention of
becoming the next addition to your list of

conquests.' She laughed humourlessly. 'I'm not even your type!' She thought of the long parade of striking brunettes.

He reached for her then, took her hand, lifted it to his mouth and kissed the palm. 'Oh, yes, you are.' He gave her a burning look. 'And as far as conquests go, that works both ways, you know. You want me as much as I want you.'

'All right, I won't deny it.' She withdrew her hand. 'There is a physical attraction, I admit. But what happens when it's over?'

He shrugged. 'Why look ahead? Let's just play it by ear, enjoy what we have together now. I've never known a woman who could set off sparks in me the way you do.' He put a hand gently on her face. 'I think it's that icy exterior,' he said softly. 'It makes the fires burning underneath twice as devastating.'

In spite of herself, Sarah was tempted. There was no denying the sheer physical power he had over her, and she had to admit that her own obvious power over this strong man who seemed to be so vulnerable to her sexually, gave her intense satisfaction.

She remembered her sister's words. 'It won't hurt you to sleep with the guy, but for God's sake don't fall in love with him.'

And that was just the trouble, she thought now bitterly. Her nature wouldn't allow her to enjoy a purely physical affair with Sloan, much as she wanted him. She had to admit to herself that she was dangerously close to falling in love with him. It was no longer a matter of protecting her virtue, but of saving her sanity, her life, her very soul.

The certainty and finality of this conviction calmed her. She turned to him, withdrawing his hand from her face.

'Sorry, Sloan,' she said softly but firmly. 'Thanks, but no, thanks. I meant it when I said I wasn't your type. It just wouldn't work for me. I'm not interested.'

His eyes narrowed at her. 'And you're a liar,' he ground out. 'Or a coward.'

'Perhaps,' she said, gazing steadily at him. 'It doesn't really matter, because my mind is made up.' She reached for the door handle.

'All right,' he said finally in a curt tone, 'have it your way. I'm not going to beg.'

Sarah got out of the car, then. There was nothing more to say. She'd stay with Margaret for a few days, then fly home and look for another job. She started up the path, then heard him call to her from the open window.

'I want to get an early start on the deposition tomorrow morning so we can get away by noon. I'll pick you up at eight.'

She couldn't believe her ears. Was he made of stone? She opened her mouth to protest. 'But . . .'

'Don't argue with me, Kincaid. Just be ready at eight.'

She heard the motor of the car start up, saw it pull away from the kerb, and stood there in the moonlight, her mouth still open, staring after him.

CHAPTER SIX

'TELL me about your husband,' said Sloan.

They were driving up the coast highway from Santa Barbara the following afternoon, with the broad blue of the Pacific Ocean at their left and the sun shining brightly overhead. Sloan had finished deposing Jack Layton well before noon, and had decided to take this longer, far more beautiful, route back to San Francisco.

'There's not much to tell,' Sarah replied shortly.

Although Sloan's manner towards her that whole morning, from the time he picked her up at her sister's house, was just as it used to be—professional, distant, curt—she was still wary. No reference had been made by either of them to last night's short, fiery encounter in the car, and

171

Sarah's thoughts were in a state of confusion.

She'd slept badly, a fact that hadn't escaped Margaret's notice at breakfast that morning. She knew her face was drawn, with dark circles under her eyes that not even a generous layer of liquid make-up could disguise.

Margaret hadn't said a word; she didn't have to. The raised eyebrows, the appraising look in her eyes, spoke volumes, and Sarah knew then that she would rather face Sloan than have to endure her sister's probing.

Of course, she had decided during that sleepless night, she would have to quit her job. After what had happened, she couldn't possibly keep working for Sloan. Yet his behaviour today was so decorous, so remote, that at one point she wondered if she hadn't dreamed the whole episode. Only the soreness of her mouth and the lingering remnants of a desire she couldn't deny told her otherwise.

'Well, he must have had a name,' Sloan

was saying. 'Or did you call him Mr
Kincaid?'

'His name was Derek,' she said curtly.

'How long were you married?'

'About a year. Less than that, actually.
We only lived together a month or two.'

He took his eyes briefly from the road
ahead and gave her an enquiring glance, but
she didn't elaborate.

'How did he die?' His eyes were back on
the road now. His voice was casual, his face
a mask behind the dark glasses.

'He was killed in an automobile accident.'
She frowned and turned to him. 'Why the
inquisition?'

He shrugged. 'No inquisition, just a
lawyer's curiosity. You've worked for me
for over five years, and I know very little
about you.'

And whose fault is that? she wanted to
retort. He was the one who treated her like a
piece of furniture. She realised she was
being perverse, claiming on the one hand
that she wanted to avoid a personal

relationship, yet resenting the fact that he had ignored her as a person until his appetite was aroused.

'Well,' she said, hoping to end the conversation, 'it was short, and not very sweet, and I only want to forget about it.'

'Yet you kept his name. You still wear his ring. Why?' She didn't answer, and he gave her another brief glance. 'Protection?' he asked softly. She still didn't answer. 'What was it, Sarah? Did he play around?'

She turned and glared at him, angry now under his probing questions. She knew his technique—she'd seen him in action often enough in the courtroom. 'Yes,' she said coldly. 'Almost from the first week. Now, are you satisfied? Can we please drop the subject?'

Dredging up the past like this only reawakened the terrible humiliation she had undergone in her brief marriage. She wanted only to forget.

'Okay, okay, I can recognise a hostile witness when I see one! I get the picture. Let's stop and have some lunch.'

Throughout lunch and for the rest of the drive up the coast, their conversation was exclusively business, mainly about the Layton case, and Sarah eventually found herself so absorbed in his battle plan for the trial, leaning heavily on Jack Layton's testimony, that she didn't even notice they had turned off the main highway. They were high on the cliffs of the Hundred Mile Drive that led past Big Sur, Monterey and Carmel, and Sloan had turned into a long narrow drive that led down the rocky cliff towards the sea.

'Where are we going?' she asked, instantly alert to danger.

'Since we're early, I thought I'd stop by and say hello to my family.' He pulled into a large circular paved parking area. Down below, nestled into the side of the cliff, was a sprawling house built of natural redwood. 'Do you mind?' he asked, shutting off the engine and turning to her.

She still sensed danger. She turned a suspicious glance on him. 'Sloan, if you think . . .'

'Now, don't argue, Kincaid,' he interrupted. 'I always stop by to see my father and sister when I'm down this way. We'll only stay an hour or so. After all, I'm paying for your time.'

Somehow, it was hard for Sarah to imagine Sloan with a father. He was so self-sufficient, so full of confidence and assurance that he seemed to have sprung full-grown from the earth or the sea. But when she met Mr Sheridan, a tall, handsome man in his early sixties, the resemblance was so striking that there was no mistaking the relationship.

He was obviously very pleased to see Sloan, and Sarah couldn't help noticing the deep affection that existed between the two men, the firm handshake when they met, the bantering, teasing tone they took with each other in conversation.

'I'm delighted to see you, my boy,' his father said, clapping him on the back. 'It's not my birthday, however, and I don't imagine you need money, so I'm at a loss as to why you've honoured us with your presence.'

They were strolling out in the beautiful garden at the back of the house. Sarah thought it was the most breathtaking sight she had ever seen, with the ocean in the background, the waves crashing up against the jutting rocks, and as far as the eye could see, what looked like hundreds of roses in full bloom.

Sloan laughed at his father's caustic remark. 'Oh, I just like to check on the decrepit old parent once in a while—see how far the senility has advanced!'

Sarah was appalled, but the older man seemed to think Sloan's jibe enormously amusing. He laughed hugely and turned to Sarah.

'You see what I've spawned?' He shook his head in mock resignation. 'And he comes from good stock, too. I'm sure if you've worked with him for some time you must be a paragon of tact, patience, endurance and fortitude. It takes a strong character to put up with him.'

'I can't argue with that,' Sarah agreed drily, 'although you forgot to mention a strong sense of self-preservation.'

Mr Sheridan laughed again. A glance at Sloan told her that he was debating whether to be amused or offended by her tart comment, but finally, in spite of himself, he had to smile. At the sight of how handsome he looked, his even white teeth flashing against his dark skin, his head thrown back, Sarah's heart began to pound dangerously.

'You see,' said Sloan, in a tone of mock resignation, 'I have my crosses to bear, too, not the least of which is insubordination.'

He was speaking to his father, but his eyes flicked at Sarah, and she was taken aback by the gentleness in them. It was as though he was making an effort to include her in the joke, to reassure her it was a joke.

His father gave her a conspiratorial wink. 'Don't pay any attention to him, Sarah. We both know he's an impossible bully, and my sympathies are entirely with you.'

He took her lightly by the arm and guided

her back up the grassy slope towards the house, their tour of the garden ended.

There was a wide covered veranda across the length of the house, and as they approached it, Sarah could see a tall, slim woman with dark hair and a hesitant manner standing by one of the wooden pillars that supported the roof. Mr Sheridan's hand tightened imperceptibly on Sarah's arm.

'Why, there's Kathleen,' he said in a forced jovial tone. 'Feeling better, darling?' he called to the woman. 'Look who's here— a surprise!'

She didn't speak or move, and as they came face to face, Sarah thought she had never seen such a hauntingly beautiful woman. Or a more nervous one. Her white hands gripped the pillar, and it was as though she was exerting enormous energy just to stay on her feet.

Sloan had moved quickly to her side as soon as he caught sight of her. Sarah watched as he put his arm around her protectively and bent to kiss her on the forehead, murmuring to her in a low tone.

'My sister Kathleen,' he said to Sarah. 'Kathy, this is Sarah Kincaid, my insubordinate secretary.'

Kathleen glanced apprehensively at Sarah, then up at her brother. She seemed to be seeking reassurance. Sloan continued to hold her, grinning down at her, and finally she managed a tremulous smile and held out a frail thin hand.

'I'm happy to meet you,' she said. Her voice sounded distant and breathless.

Sarah took the hand. It trembled in hers like a frightened bird. She gave it a firm squeeze, then let go.

'Well, Kathy,' said her father in a hearty tone, 'do you think Mrs Anthony can find enough scraps to go around to feed these two travellers?'

Kathleen gave her father a startled look and started to stammer out a reply when Sloan interrupted.

'Sorry, Dad, we've got to be going soon.'

'Well, a drink then, at least,' his father said. Oddly, he seemed more relieved than disappointed. He looked at Kathleen. 'Kathy, maybe you could show Sarah to the powder room,' he suggested in a gentle tone.

'Yes, of course.' Every word, Sarah thought as she followed Kathleen into the house, every movement, seemed to cost the poor woman tremendous effort.

As she washed her hands and combed her hair, Sarah wondered what in the world was wrong with her. She really was beautiful, with Sloan's coarse dark hair streaked with grey, cut short in an unruly mop that intensified the impression of fragility on the pale face. The eyes were the same, a brown so deep as to seem black, but where in Sloan's the brooding quality denoted strength, in Kathleen's it verged on terror.

They had one drink, out on the wide veranda, and during the whole time Kathleen sat twisting a handkerchief in her lap, lost in a world of her own, not uttering a sound. When Sloan spoke to her, she jumped.

'Have you been painting, Kathy?' he repeated slowly, gently, with infinite patience.

Sarah saw the first spark of genuine interest light up Kathleen's dark eyes. 'Yes,' she said, her voice pathetically eager. 'Yes, I have, a little.'

'May I see?' Sloan asked.

'Yes,' came the breathless reply. 'I'll show you.'

When they were gone, Sloan's father turned to Sarah and gave her a frankly appraising gaze. His eyes were kind, however, and Sarah met them without discomfort. Finally, he spoke.

'You mustn't mind Kathleen. She had a serious mental breakdown some years ago, and never quite recovered.' He smiled at the look of concern on Sarah's face. 'She's perfectly able to live a fairly normal life, so long as she feels secure. She's quite safe here with me, and Mrs Anthony helps me look after her.' He paused.

'I'm very sorry,' Sarah said helplessly. 'I had no idea—Sloan never said anything. She's so beautiful . . .' Her voice trailed off.

Mr Sheridan held up a hand. 'I'm not surprised Sloan didn't mention it. They were very close—still are, in a way. What does surprise me is that he brought you here at all. It's the first time he's done it.'

'The first time? I don't understand.'

He sighed. 'Sloan is very attached to his sister. And fiercely protective.' He chuckled. 'I know my son has had a very, shall we say, active and varied social life, but he's never brought any of his friends here to meet Kathleen.' He leaned closer to her, their heads almost touching. His eyes were kind, but asked a question. 'You must be very special to him.'

'Oh, no,' she replied quickly, too quickly. 'I'm only his secretary.'

He gave her a disbelieving look and opened his mouth to speak, but at that moment Sloan reappeared. He was alone.

'If you're trying to seduce Sarah, Dad,'

he drawled from the doorway, 'let me tell you it can't be done.'

Sarah flushed a deep red and glared at him. How dare he? She wanted to go to him and slap that mocking grin off his face.

His father put a comforting hand on Sarah's shoulder and gave Sloan a scathing glance.

'Well, if those are the tactics you use,' he remarked lightly, 'I can see why you've failed.' He turned to Sarah. 'I'd say that remark deserves at least a week off with pay!'

Sarah had to smile, and when she glanced at Sloan and saw the abashed look on his face, just like a chastened schoolboy, her grin broadened. She turned gratefully to Mr Sheridan.

'When I first met you,' she said clearly, 'I thought you and Sloan were very much alike. Now I see that somehow your finer qualities didn't quite make it through to him.'

Mr Sheridan threw back his head and roared.

'All right, Kincaid,' Sloan snapped, glowering at her. 'You've had your fun. Now let's get going.'

By the time they reached the City and had crossed the bridge to the Oakland side, dusk was falling. They had made the short trip up from Carmel in total silence, each absorbed in his own thoughts.

Sarah had seen a new side of Sloan that afternoon at his father's house, a side she never dreamed existed. The deep affection he felt for his father, the ease of their relationship, but most of all his gentleness with Kathleen, all were in direct contradiction to the cold, ruthless man she knew so well.

And what was the significance of his father's remark that this was the first time Sloan had brought a woman to meet his family? Mr Sheridan had said she must be very special to Sloan for him to have done such a thing, but Sarah found that hard to believe.

He wanted to have an affair with her, that much was clear. He even seemed to want that more than he wanted her services as a secretary. Glancing at him now out of the corner of her eye as they came off the bridge, his brooding profile, eyes fixed firmly on the road ahead, she had to admit to herself that she was sorely tempted.

Just being with him made her pulses race and her heart sing. She wanted more than anything to be in those powerful arms again, to feel his lips on hers, and had to stop herself from reaching out now and touching the dark hair, the strong nose, the large competent hands lying lightly on the steering wheel.

To have an affair with him, however brief, would add a dimension to her barren life, enrich it beyond her wildest dreams. She had never wanted Derek the way she wanted Sloan Sheridan. Just because of that fact, however, she was afraid the end would be even more devastating, and she could never go through that again.

She saw only one way out. It was a bleak one. Not only would she lose Sloan as a lover, but also as a boss. A bitter choice, but it was the only answer. She could either walk out of his life now, in every way, or be destroyed eventually. She would have to make him see this.

She turned to him. 'Sloan . . .'

'Sarah . . .' he said at the same time. He glanced at her, but she remained silent. 'I want to explain to you about Kathleen,' he went on when he saw she wasn't going to speak.

They were in front of her house now, a quiet street of small, well-kept cottages and gardens. There were sprinklers running on the patches of lawn in front of the houses, children playing on the sidewalk. A boy rode by on his bicycle, a small dog yapping at his heels. Across the street a neighbour, Mrs Dugan, was out watering her roses, her eyes firmly fixed on the luxurious Mercedes.

'Would you like a little supper?' Sarah

asked. They had a lot to talk about. It had to be done some time, and they couldn't do it in the office or on the telephone or out here in the car for all the world to see. 'Nothing fancy,' she added hastily. 'Just a grilled cheese sandwich and a salad.'

Sloan gave her an odd look. 'We could go out to eat if you'd like.'

'No.' A restaurant was too public.

'All right, then. Let's see if you're as good at cooking as you are at everything else.'

She gave him a swift glance to see if he was making fun of her, but his expression was pleasant and quite serious. She sighed inwardly. This agreeable Sloan was a lot harder to resist than the abrupt, mocking one she knew so well.

'This is very pleasant,' he said as he glanced around her living room with its cool muted colours, dark woods and pastel prints on the off-white walls. 'It looks just like you.'

She led the way into the kitchen. 'Is that a compliment or a criticism?' she called over her shoulder.

He stood in the small kitchen, filling it with his presence. 'Why, a compliment, of course. Have you ever known me to be critical?'

She whirled around and gave him a disbelieving look. He grinned.

'Sit down,' she said, gesturing to the birch gateleg table by the window. 'Would you like a beer? Martini?'

'A beer would be fine. Join me. The dinner can wait.'

She got the beer and two glasses and sat down across from him. 'You pour. I always end up with too much foam.'

After he had poured the beer, Sloan took off his jacket, loosened his tie and lit a cigarette. He leaned tiredly back in his chair and sighed contentedly, then drank his beer in silence for a minute or two.

'About Kathleen,' he said at last.

'Your father told me she'd had a

breakdown some years ago.' Sarah wanted him to know that, 'But he didn't elaborate.'

'Well, I'm not going to burden you with our family problems, but I think you might sympathise with her experience.' He took another swallow of beer and gave her a penetrating look. 'And perhaps profit from it. It's similar in some ways to your own.'

'My experience?' She kept her voice steady with an effort, suddenly afraid of what was coming.

'Yes,' he said succinctly. There was a note of challenge in his voice. He ground out his cigarette in the ashtray. 'Kathleen has money of her own, and before her—illness—she was very beautiful. Still is, in a shadowy way. Only, oddly, like many beautiful women, she never quite believed it, never had the confidence in her own attractions that many less beautiful women develop so easily.'

He gave her a meaningful look then, but she didn't speak. He went on, his voice low and clear, choosing his words carefully.

'She fell in love. Our mother died when we were children. Dad and I did our best to protect her, but what do men know about a woman's needs? We didn't like the guy, but we were afraid to insist too strongly that he was only after her money because she had so little confidence to begin with.'

'And he was?' Sarah asked softly. 'Just after her money?'

Sloan sighed deeply and took another long swallow of beer. He frowned. 'I think he loved her, I really do. But he was weak. Kathleen is—was—a very intense person, artistic, romantic. George wanted fun, bright lights, glamour. He found it—but not with Kathleen.'

'I see.' Sarah's heart ached for her. She knew too well that feeling of desolation when the romance crumbled and the dream faded.

'Well, in any event,' he went on brusquely, straightening up in his chair and resting his elbows on the table, 'he was unfaithful—several times. There was a divorce, and Kathleen withdrew into a shell she's never quite come out of.' He finished his beer in one long gulp and set the glass down hard on the table. 'It's such a waste,' he said bitterly, 'such a tragic waste.'

Sarah got up from the table and started preparing their dinner. Silently, she handed Sloan another beer, hardly able to look at him. Finally, after she had set the sandwiches to grill and was tossing the salad, she spoke, her back to him.

'You're telling me that I've done the same thing,' she said tonelessly.

'No.' His voice was flat. 'You're obviously made of stronger stuff than Kathleen. You handle a demanding job, keep up your own home. You function in the world.'

She turned slowly to face him. 'Well then?'

He shook his head slowly from side to side. 'It's still a waste. She's running from the world. You're running from yourself.'

Sarah began to feel cornered under his probing analysis, like an animal caught in a trap. She didn't like the unpleasant sensation of panic that began to rise up in her, and she made herself grow rigid, controlled.

'Why the sudden concern for my welfare?' she bit out in a frosty voice as she set the meal down on the table.

Sloan's eyes narrowed at her. 'Just that, believe it or not. Concern.'

She sat down again and gave a dry, hollow laugh. 'And of course, nowhere in that devious mind of yours is the slightest idea that predicting all these disastrous consequences will convince me to hop into bed with you. Something like therapy.'

Sarah took a bite of sandwich. It tasted like cardboard in her dry mouth. She washed it down with a gulp of beer and took another bite.

'No,' he said shortly, 'there isn't.' He chewed thoughtfully, gazing at her all the while. 'I don't have to stoop to tricks like that to get you into my bed,' he said coolly at last, 'and you know it.'

She began to clear the table. 'You can

forget that,' she said. Her voice was calm, in spite of her inner turmoil. 'It will never happen.'

His hand shot out and grasped her by the wrist so hard that she dropped the plate she was holding. She darted her eyes at him. His face was twisted with barely-concealed anger.

'Why are you being so damned stubborn?' he demanded in a tight voice. He pulled her down on to his lap, his arms around her. She gazed up at him with frightened eyes. He kissed her briefly, but seductively. 'Tell me that does nothing to you,' he murmured. He put a hand firmly on her breast. 'Or this.'

Shafts of fire shot through her at his touch, his kiss, and it took all her strength to meet his eyes coolly and calmly.

'No,' she said, 'it does nothing to me. Now, please let me go. I can grow my own red roses.'

Immediately his face became a mask and he dropped his hands. Sarah stood up and smoothed her hair, her skirt, and calmly began to carry dishes to the sink.

'I think it would be best if I left the firm,' she said over her shoulder. 'Surely you see I can't keep working for you now?'

She started rinsing the dishes, waiting for his reply. He was silent for so long that she finally turned around, drying her hands on the dishtowel.

He was standing behind of his chair. He had put his jacket on and was tightening his tie in an easy, graceful gesture. He's so tall, she thought, weakening, so damned attractive. He makes the whole room come alive.

'I think you're right,' he said at last. 'I'll hate to lose you, Sarah—in more ways than one—but I can see your mind is made up.'

'Yes,' she said in a low voice, 'it is.'

She felt sick with regret as visions of a bleak dismal future opened up before her, but she had no choice. She couldn't bear a meaningless affair with him, loving him the way she did, and working with him now as though nothing had happened between them would be impossible, a daily torment.

'Will you do me one favour?' he went on. 'I know it's a lot to ask, but it really is important.'

'What is it?'

'Will you stay just until the Alvarez trial?' She hesitated. 'I really need you, Sarah,' he went on. 'It'll only be for another month. The trial comes up the first of August. You can quit a few weeks before that, or at least take your vacation then, decide for sure if you still want to leave.'

She looked at him with troubled eyes. 'I don't know, Sloan,' she said slowly.

'Look, I know I haven't been a model boss . . .'

She shook her head. 'It's not that. You know it's not that.'

'All right,' he growled, 'and I broke my promise to keep my hands off.' He drew in a deep breath. 'I'm not going to apologise for that. Whether you think so or not, it was a compliment. And I won't make any more promises I can't keep. I'll be gone from the office most of the time. We'll hardly see each other.' He paused. 'And I do need you, Sarah.'

Every instinct warned her not to give in, but she knew he was right. He did need her, and she couldn't just leave him in the lurch like this with an mportant trial coming up. She thought of poor Dr Alvarez, with the prospect of a career in ruins, and knew she had a responsibility to do what little she could to help him.

'A month, then,' she said at last with a little sigh. She looked at him. 'One month.'

CHAPTER SEVEN

DURING the next three weeks, Sarah barely had time to catch her breath, much less worry about Sloan's interest in her. The burden of his other cases fell on her, as he and Warren spent most of their time preparing the Alvarez case for trial.

By now, the middle of July, all the discovery work had been done—depositions taken, interrogatories filed, documents inspected on both sides. Poor Dr Alvarez seemed to shrink more each time he came into the office, and Sarah was finally convinced she had done the right thing in staying on. She knew the case didn't really depend on a secretary, but with her there to take much of the burden off Sloan's shoulders, it left him free to give all his attention to the trial.

He and Warren were deep now in preparing their trial brief, jury instructions, and deciding which witnesses to subpoena to testify at trial. Sloan was leaning heavily on Jack Layton's testimony, and he and Warren went over the transcript of the deposition taken in Santa Barbara last month with a fine tooth comb over and over again.

According to Jack Layton, Martha was really sixteen, not fourteen as her lawyer claimed, and he had sworn under oath that Mrs Layton not only had been unfaithful to him during their marriage, but had encouraged Martha to engage in premature sexual activity in an attempt to enhance her own attractions.

'That's terrible,' Sarah said to Sloan one day as he was dictating excerpts from the Layton deposition to include in his trial brief. 'What kind of mother pushes her daughter into growing up too soon?'

'A mother who sees herself losing her own attractiveness and wants to relive her youth through the girl,' was Sloan's wry comment.

Sarah shook her head, remembering her own careful upbringing. 'How times have changed.' She laughed. 'I can recall Mother and Dad waiting up for Margaret, checking on her every move, grounding her for weeks at a time when she came home late from a date!'

They were in Sloan's office. It was late afternoon, a bright sunny day. The air-conditioning hummed distantly, and traffic noises drifted up from the street. Typewriters clacked from the outer office. Telephones rang.

'Only Margaret?' Sloan asked pleasantly, with a hint of a smile.

Sarah dropped her eyes to her notebook. 'She was the popular one,' she murmured.

Sloan was leaning back in his swivel chair, his legs spread apart, a pencil tapping on the desk. 'And you were the good little girl, I take it.'

Refusing to be baited, she gave him a cool smile. 'Something like that.'

Looking at him now, so relaxed, so

elegant and handsome in his dark suit and flashing white shirt, she realised that he still had the power to set her pulses racing. Only another week, she thought, and I'll be able to leave, probably to walk out of his life forever.

Is that really what I want? she wondered. She looked at him again. He had turned his chair around and was leaning over his desk, his elbows propped on the broad top, one hand cupping his chin, the other idly turning the pages of the Layton transcript.

By now there was no doubt in her mind that she was hopelessly in love with him, that when she left, as she knew she must, her life would be empty and meaningless without him.

Once again, she wondered if she wasn't wrong about her refusal to have an affair with him. Since the Santa Barbara trip when she had agreed to work with him for another month, his behaviour towards her was a model of circumspection and propriety. Not by a word or a glance did he indicate in any way that his interest in her was anything but professional.

As far as she knew there had been no woman in his life since she'd sent the standard two dozen red roses and card to Ariel Boone, and that had been two months ago.

She had one more week to go on her temporary return. One more week of seeing him every day, hearing his voice, being close to him. One more week of torment. One more week of longing to touch him, to tell him she loved him, to feel his arms around her.

As far as the rest of the office was concerned, she would only be going on her vacation. She hadn't come to a firm decision yet about whether she would come back to work for Sloan or not. In a way she wanted to, just to be near him, but because of her own wayward feelings for him, she doubted they could ever resume their old working relationship.

*   *   *

On her last Friday in the office, Sarah spent most of the day tidying her desk and reorganising her files to make it easier for her replacement to step in and take over. Ginny, Warren's secretary, was perfectly capable of handling things for a few weeks, and Sarah had gone over Sloan's other cases with her carefully, filling her in on details and typing lists of pertinent facts for each one. If Sloan would give Ginny half a chance, she thought, she'd make a fine secretary for him if I do decide not to come back.

Luckily, Sloan had been gone all day. Jack Layton had been in an automobile accident, and Sloan and Warren had flown down to Santa Barbara to make sure he would be well enough to testify at the trial in two weeks. Sarah was relieved that she wouldn't have to face him on her last day. She couldn't have borne that, she thought now as she made one last survey of her neat desk and orderly files.

It was just after five o'clock. The office

had been virtually empty since four-thirty, typical on a fine Friday afternoon in July. Everyone wanted to get an early start to the weekend, and when the lawyers left, their secretaries were not far behind.

She gathered her personal belongings together and walked down the long corridor and out to the reception room for perhaps the last time. Although that possibility hadn't really sunk in yet, she still felt bereft and disorientated, as though she were leaving the warm security of home for a bleak unknown.

Nancy was still at the reception desk, which stayed open until five-thirty. As Sarah passed by, the girl gave her a frankly envious look.

'Have a nice vacation, Sarah,' she called to her. 'Lucky you!'

'Thanks, Nancy.' She hesitated. She wondered if she should say a permanent goodbye, but decided not to.

'Going anyplace special?'

'I'm not sure yet.' She continued on to

the bank of elevators and punched the down button. 'Don't work too hard!'

The elevator came. Sarah got on, and was whisked downward, and wondered sadly if she would ever do this again.

The telephone was ringing when Sarah stepped inside her house that evening, and she ran into the kitchen to answer it.

'Hello.'

'Sarah,' came Sloan's urgent voice, 'I know this is officially your vacation, but I need to ask you one more favour.'

At the first sound of that familiar voice, Sarah's heart started to pound. She had thought never to hear it again. She sat down weakly.

'Jack Layton is in a really bad way down here.' He was calling from Santa Barbara, then, she thought, and automatically reached for the pad and pencil.

'Will he be well enough to testify at the trial?' Her voice was brisk and professional, falling easily into the old pattern.

Sloan grunted. 'No,' he said in a curt tone. 'That's not my problem, though—I can always get a continuance. But he got really banged up in that accident, and isn't expected to live.'

Sarah drew in her breath sharply. Jack Layton was Sloan's key witness. Without him, the chances of getting Dr Alvarez acquitted dropped dramatically. They could still use his sworn deposition testimony at trial, even if he didn't live, but Sloan's skill in a courtroom, actually confronting a witness, was his greatest asset.

'I'm leaving Langley down here,' Sloan went on, 'and that's why I need you. As a last resort, he and I were going over to Marin County tomorrow to try to get some candid photos of Martha Layton and her mother. Jack told us when we took his deposition last month that he suspected they either had a couple of guys living there with them or threw some pretty wild parties. If I can get pictures of that, it would go a long way towards helping the doctor's case.' He paused. 'I can't do it alone, Sarah, and Langley's got to stay here with Jack Layton. Will you help me?'

'Of course,' she said without hesitation. 'What do you want me to do?'

'Good girl!' he breathed. 'I knew you wouldn't let me down.'

He told her he would pick her up at three o'clock the next afternoon. They would drive over to Marin County, where the Layton women lived on a secluded bluff overlooking the Golden Gate and the small town of Sausalito. With luck, they could find a secluded spot nearby and get some photographs of how they really lived.

'And wear something suitable for hiking,' he added as an afterthought before he hung up. 'Langley and I reconnoitred the place a few weeks ago, and it's pretty rugged.'

It wasn't until she'd hung up the phone that Sarah began to have second thoughts. Just that afternoon she had accepted that she might never seen Sloan Sheridan again, and now she was proposing to spend an afternoon with him alone. Would she never learn?

Yet, as she lay in bed that night thinking it over, what else could she have done? Said no? It was unthinkable that she turn him down now when he seemed to need her help so desperately.

One last time, she thought with a sigh just before she drifted off to sleep, and that will be the end of it.

Sloan picked her up in front of her house the next afternoon promptly at three o'clock. In obedience to his instructions, she had worn a pair of jeans and a cotton shirt. Her hair was coiled neatly at the back of her neck, and she had a notebook and supply of pencils tucked in her bag.

Her second thoughts of the evening before returned in full force the moment she set eyes on him waiting for her inside the car. He was wearing snugly-fitting black denim trousers with a pale grey cotton knit shirt that moulded every muscle of his lean taut back and chest. His tanned arms were bare, and an irresistible flood of desire washed over her when she saw the way his strong arm muscles moved under his skin as he manoeuvred the car through the traffic, over the Bay Bridge, through the City and out to the Golden Gate.

As he drove, he outlined his plans for their excursion in the same flat, curt tones she was used to, and her uneasiness gradually vanished as she concentrated on what he wanted her to do.

'I need you to help me with the camera equipment,' he explained as they made their way up into the hills above Sausalito, 'but mainly as a witness in case something happens to the film.' He gave her a sidelong glance. 'That is, if we're in luck and see something worth using in court.'

'Just what is it you're hoping to find?' They had entered a state park now, and were driving up a narrow road, past the picnickers and campers on the grassy slopes, towards a small forest of dense evergreens.

'According to Jack Layton, the two ladies are in the habit of entertaining their male guests at some pretty wild parties. Their house is very secluded with a high chain link fence around it. It's built out on a bluff with only those woods up ahead behind it, virtually inaccessible.'

The paved road ended abruptly, to be replaced by a narrow dirt path. Sloan pulled the car into a clearing behind a clump of mountain ash, where it would be well hidden from the road below, and shut off the engine. He turned to her, his jaw set, every muscle tense under the knit shirt.

'There's no danger,' he said quietly, 'but it's rugged country and we could have a long wait. Also, there's an outside chance you might have to testify in court as a witness to what you see here. That is, if we see anything worthwhile.' He gave her a penetrating look. 'Are you still game?'

Sarah met his eyes briefly. The only danger she was concerned about was in the man sitting beside her in the car. He was so

close that she could see the little pulse
beating at his temple just where the thick
hair began, the lines at the corners of his
eyes, the hollow of his throat above the
open-necked shirt.

'Let's go,' she said.

He flashed her a brief smile and reached
over to grab a camera, binoculars and a pair
of leather gloves from the back seat. They
got out of the car and started walking up the
dirt path through the trees and thick
covering of underbrush.

After a good half hour of silent, dusty
trudging, Sloan stopped short and went
some distance into the woods.

'You wait here,' he said. 'I want to make
sure I have the right spot.'

He reappeared a few seconds later and
beckoned to her. Sarah stepped off the path
to follow him through the dense thicket,
picking her way carefully over tree stumps
and fallen logs. Ahead of her, Sloan,
wearing the leather gloves, stopped every so
often to hold back the encroachng branches

for her, but still, by the time they reached the tall chain link fence surrounding the Layton property, Sarah was hot, dusty and perspiring, and her bare arms were covered with tiny scratches.

They stood behind a clump of broom growing along the fence and looked down into the rear of the sprawling pink stucco house. There was a sparkling blue swimming pool surrounded by a wide paved area, with several chaises and deck chairs scattered about. It looked pleasant and inviting and totally deserted.

Sarah gave Sloan an enquiring look, and he shrugged his shoulders. 'We'll just have to wait,' he said in a low voice.

They waited. While Sarah held the camera equipment, Sloan took the binoculars and trained them on the house below. An hour passed. Sarah ached all over from her cramped position, squatting by the fence. She began to worry that it would get dark before there was any activity down there. It was almost seven o'clock. Only a few more hours of daylight left.

It was terribly hot and still, with only the buzz of insects, an occasional crackling of a falling branch, and Sloan's quiet breathing to break the silence. Sarah shifted her position and leaned back up against a tree trunk. She closed her eyes and started to doze off when a sudden loud blast of rock music pierced the stillness.

Sarah's eyes flew open and she looked at Sloan. He handed her the binoculars and took the camera from her, his eyes alight, his mouth grim and set.

She looked down through the binoculars. Some people had come out of the house and were standing around the pool. Two women, dressed in brief wisps of bikinis, and two men in bathing trunks. They all had glasses in their hands and were passing around a cigarette, obviously marijuana.

Soon they began to dance to the beat of the raucous music. Sarah could hear their laughter drifting up, punctuated by screams as the dancing became more frenzied. She was appalled when she recognised Martha Layton as the younger of the two women. This was the demure little girl fresh out of the convent? What a joke!

Poor Dr Alvarez, she thought. She could hardly bear to watch as the scene below became more suggestive, bodies twined together now, glistening in the sun, but she made herself take in every sickening detail.

She glanced at Sloan, clicking away with his camera, a telescopic lens attached to it. He was down on his haunches, his whole body taut. At last he put the camera down.

'Okay,' he said, 'I got what I wanted. Let's go.'

He forged ahead of her, breaking the trail again, and Sarah stumbled after him, panting from the effort to keep up. It seemed much worse going down than it had been coming up. Sloan seemed to be in a tearing hurry.

'Come on,' he urged her, looking back as he held a branch for her. 'I want to get out of here before dark.'

It was the old Sloan, Sarah thought, her

temper rising. Get the job done and never mind who gets hurt. Well, wasn't that what she wanted?

'I'm coming as fast as I can,' she said evenly. 'I'm not used to this.'

In an effort to quicken her pace, she tripped over a tree root and fell sideways smack in the middle of a patch of brambles. As the sharp thorns tore at her hair and the tender skin of her face and arms, she could feel panic rising up in her. In her struggle to get free, she became entangled further in the clinging branches, and really terrified now, she cried out.

Then she heard Sloan's voice. 'Calm down, Kincaid,' he barked at her. 'Just quit thrashing around—you're only making it worse.'

She gazed up at him with frightened eyes, his sharp tone bringing her back to her senses. With all her strength she made her body go still, resisting the impulse to fight off the wickedly strong, piercing vines that held her prisoner.

Calmly and competently he set to work. With the leather gloves on his hands, the thorns were no obstacle to him, and soon he had at least snapped the branches that were entangled in her hair and tearing at her face. Sarah sighed with relief when her head was free at last.

He was working now on the thorny vines pulling at her blouse, pushing them aside carefully, methodically, so that finally the upper part of her body was free. Sloan took her hands and pulled her up.

'Come on, now, I think you can make it. Your jeans are heavy enough to take the thorns without tearing.'

She closed her eyes, still shuddering, and allowed him to drag her to safety. She could feel the sharp thorns scratching at her jeans, but none of them penetrated, and at last she was free. With a sob of relief, she fell trembling into Sloan's arms.

He held her gently, comforting her, stroking her shaking shoulders and tangled hair, murmuring soothing sounds until at last she sighed and slumped gratefully against the hard chest.

'Okay now?' he asked at last, tilting her chin up.

She forced out a weak grin, sniffled a little and wiped her eyes with the back of her hand. 'Okay.'

'Then we'd better get out of here.'

The sun had gone down, and there was a chill in the air. Sarah shivered. She looked down at her tattered blouse, scant covering in the damp chill of the evening, and her eyes widened in horror as she saw that the thin blouse had been torn to shreds by the brambles. The buttons had been pulled off and what little material was left intact was gaping open, revealing a lacy bra and a good portion of her full breast.

Quickly she hugged her arms across her chest, a deep flush spreading across her face. She glanced at Sloan, whose own shirt was slightly torn. He was grinning broadly.

'Not exactly Adam and Eve in the garden,' he said in a light tone, 'but close.'

When she didn't respond, he laughed. 'Oh, come on, Sarah, I've seen less than you've got on at the beach. Let's go now, we're almost at the path.'

This time Sloan moved more slowly and Sarah kept close behind him. When they finally reached the path, she felt so weak with relief that she had trouble remaining on her feet. Sloan gave her one sharp look, then swooped her up in his arms.

'No, Sloan,' she protested feebly as he began striding down the path. 'Just give me a minute—I can walk.'

'Like hell you can,' he muttered, and continued on.

She knew it was useless to argue with him, and relaxed against him gratefully, more shaken by her encounter with the brambles than she cared to admit. It was a relief just to let herself be carried along by this strong determined man.

At the car, he set her down, and she leaned weakly up against it while he unlocked the door and stowed their gear in the back seat. She felt dizzy, and there was a strange sticky sensation on her back, which had borne the brunt of her fall. She started shivering again.

'Turn around,' he said grimly. Wordlessly, she obeyed. 'God, Sarah,' he exclaimed after a long silence, 'your back is covered with blood!'

He pulled out a car blanket from the back seat and draped it around her. Gently he helped her into the car, then went round and got in beside her.

The last thing she remembered was the sound of the car engine starting up and Sloan's arm coming round her to pull her close to him. Her head drooped on his shoulder, and she closed her eyes.

When she woke up, aching and disorientated, her back smarting painfully, the car had stopped. She could smell a cigarette burning. She opened her eyes and saw Sloan sitting beside her, smoking quietly. Her head was still on his shoulder, the blanket still wrapped around her. She sat up.

'Feeling any better?' His voice was low and calm, but with an undertone of anxiety.

'I think so,' she replied. She looked around. They were parked on a quiet city street along a steep hill in a neighbourhood of typical San Francisco row houses. 'Where are we?'

'My place,' was the brief reply. 'Your back needs immediate attention. I was just waiting for you to wake up.'

Sarah thought this over. He stirred and put his hand on the car door. She reached out to stop him, and winced as a shaft of fire blazed across her back.

'No,' she said weakly, 'I'm all right. Please take me home.'

'Sure you're all right,' he said in an exasperated tone. 'I can see that by the look on your face. Now just do as I say and don't argue. I'll see to your back and get you to a doctor if you need one, then I'll take you home. All right?'

'All right,' she said at last. She knew it was useless to protest, and she didn't have the strength to fight him now.

She allowed him to lead her up the narrow concrete front stoop, into the house and up a flight of stairs to a large, immaculate bedroom. It looked just like him, she thought as she gazed around at the stark uncluttered furnishings. She saw a large bed with a heavy bedspread of a rich brown material. On the white walls hung a few impressionistic paintings that she guessed were Kathleen's work. There was a mahogany chest of drawers, thick beige carpeting, bedside tables and functional lamps.

Sloan had gone into the adjoining bathroom, and she could hear water running. When he came back he held out a soft white terrycloth robe.

'Get into the tub,' he said firmly. 'I'll go down to the kitchen and heat up some soup. Unless you need some help?' He gave her a wicked grin.

'No, thank you,' she said primly, still huddled in the blanket. 'I can manage quite well on my own.'

She could hear his laughter floating back as he went down the stairs, and once inside the bathroom she locked the door firmly behind her.

Stripping off the tattered shirt was a painful chore, with the congealing blood sticking to it, and the first touch of the hot bathwater on her sore back was excruciating. Gradually, though, as she relaxed, the fragrant, sudsy water became more soothing. She soaked for a long time. The warm bath loosened the aching muscles, and the tension began to ebb slowly out of her. She began to feel quite like herself again.

And also, she thought, quite apprehensive. Here she was, after all these weeks of successfully avoiding any personal contact with Sloan, alone with him in his house with only tattered rags for clothing.

She got out of the tub and dried herself gingerly. The towelling robe was miles too big for her, but she wrapped it tightly around her and tied it securely at the waist. She unlocked the bathroom door, and peered tentatively into the bedroom. It was empty.

She found her bag on a chair and took out her comb. Her hair was still so snarled from her encounter with the thorns that combing through the tangles brought tears to her eyes. She stood in front of the dressing-table mirror, sticking at it, until finally the dark gold strands fell smoothly about her face, and she could gaze at her reflection without wincing.

She leaned forward to examine herself more closely. There were scratches on her face, but the bath had washed them clean. It was her back that hurt so badly.

Then suddenly, in the mirror, she saw Sloan standing behind her, his black eyes fastened on her reflection with an intense brooding look. She straightened up and slowly turned around.

'Here,' he said handing her a steaming mug, 'drink this.'

She stretched out a hand and took it from him. He watched her as she drank, and when she was through he took the empty mug from her and set it down on the dresser. He had changed his torn clothes and was wearing a white dress shirt, open at the neck, the cuffs rolled back. His thick hair was a little damp, as though he had just showered.

They stood in silence facing each other for several long seconds. The tension growing up between them crackled in the air like a charge of electricity. Sarah's heart began to thud painfully. She looked away uneasily, wanting to go, longing to stay.

'How are you feeling now?' His light tone sounded forced.

'Fine,' she said brightly. 'Just fine. If you can give me something to wear and take me home . . .'

'Not yet,' he interrupted sharply. 'I want to have a look at that back first.'

Sarah stiffened and narrowed her eyes at

him. He gave her a disgusted look.

'For God's sake, Sarah, I'm not going to rape you! Don't you know that by now?'

She nodded dumbly. How could she tell him that it wasn't his desire she was afraid of, but her own? She was finding their closeness alone here in his bedroom oppressive, unsettling.

'Please,' she murmured, her hazel eyes pleading, 'just take me home.'

He reached one hand out to her, as if to reassure her, then dropped it. 'I will,' he said softly. 'I promise. I've found some clothes that might fit you.' He pointed to a neat pile on a chair. 'Just let me take a look at that back first and get some antiseptic on it.'

Finally, reluctantly, she allowed him to lead her into the bathroom. He reached into the medicine cabinet and took out a tube of antiseptic cream, then put his hands on her shoulders and turned her around so that her back was to him.

'This stuff is supposed to take the sting

out as well as kill all the nasty germs,' he said in a conversational tone.

He was standing behind her, his hands still resting on her shoulders. He left them there for a few seconds without speaking. Then, briskly, he said, 'Don't panic now, Sarah, but I can't very well get at your back with this robe on. You'll have to take it off. Just pretend I'm the doctor.'

CHAPTER EIGHT

SARAH turned her head and gave Sloan a quick glance over her shoulder.

'You must be joking!' she commented drily. Nothing on earth would induce her to strip off that robe in front of him. Not if her back was flayed raw. 'Just slip it down over my shoulders,' she went on firmly, 'and stop when I tell you to.'

She looked at him. He seemed to be trying hard not to smile, but he managed to set his features in an expression of suitable gravity and nodded his agreement.

'All right, you're the boss. But don't blame me if you get an infection just because you're too modest to let me do the job properly.'

She opened her mouth to deliver a stinging retort, then shut it again. He was only baiting her. 'I wouldn't dream of it,' she said tartly, turning away from him again. 'Now, can we just get on with it and get it over with?'

She waited, her eyes shut tight, her hands firmly clutching the robe in front of her, steeling herself for the coming ordeal. She felt his fingers grasp the neck of the robe and tug gently at it, pulling it down over her shoulders. She went rigid as the knuckles of his hand grazed her skin and held the loosened robe together more securely.

'That's far enough,' she muttered in a tight voice.

'For God's sake,' he protested, 'your shoulder blades are barely visible, and they're a mess.' He tugged at the robe.

'That's far enough!' she repeated in a firmer tone. 'You don't have to see to spread it on.'

He sighed dramatically and she felt his breath on the nape of her neck as he exhaled. 'All right,' came his elaborately weary voice, 'but don't blame me . . .'

'I won't blame you for anything!' she cried, her nerves beginning to give way. 'Now, will you please get on with it?'

I must have been out of my mind to agree to this, she grumbled to herself as she waited for him to begin. This whole miserable day was an act of sheer stupidity. I do the man a favour, out of the kindness of my heart, and does he appreciate it? Of course not. Why was he taking so long? She couldn't stand much more of this.

'What are you doing?' she muttered at last. 'Manufacturing the stuff yourself?'

'I'm taking off the cap,' he said in a broadly patient tone, 'and squeezing the ointment out of the tube on to my hand. Is that all right?'

Sarah opened her mouth to reply, but the sudden touch of his hand coming down on her back at last stopped her cold. She drew in her breath sharply. The cream felt like ice on her warm back, but her shock was primarily due to the sensations aroused in her at his touch.

I should never have agreed to this, she thought, as his hands moved gently over her shoulders. Surely the bath had cleaned the wounds thoroughly enough? They didn't even hurt any more. She began to suspect that Sloan had exaggerated the seriousness of her injuries. The scratches on her face and arms were barely visible.

Still, she was sore, and the gentle kneading did help. The tight muscles of her back and shoulders began to relax, and she closed her eyes and let her head drop forward as his hands continued their gentle, rhythmic stroking.

Sloan, she thought, an image of him forming in her mind. This was Sloan Sheridan, the cold distant scourge of her working life, the tall man with the forbidding manner and dangerous eyes. Dangerous? How could she ever have thought him a threat? Why had she resisted him so stubbornly? Wasn't this what she really wanted?

Her thoughts continued in this vein as the

soothing hands did their work and lulled her into a pleasant euphoria. She loosened her hold on the robe and let it slip farther down her arms. She had already admitted to herself that she was in love with him, hadn't she? What difference did it make that it would only be a short affair? Why not enjoy it while it lasted? Wouldn't she regret it more if she rejected this opportunity than if she gave in to her own feelings now and was discarded later when he tired of her?

Then all thinking ceased. All she was conscious of now was the way Sloan's touch made her feel, the gradual quickening of his breath on her skin, her own madly racing pulses.

Suddenly his hands stopped and came to rest on her shoulders. His lips came down tentatively on the nape of her neck, then more firmly when she didn't resist. She made her body go still, waiting. He pulled her long hair aside, and his mouth moved to her ear.

'Sarah,' he whispered. 'Sarah.'

Still she neither spoke nor moved. There was a humming, buzzing noise in her head and a warmth coursed through her body. Lightheaded, she leaned back against him. Dimly she heard him draw in his breath sharply, and his arms came around her neck, pulling her back closer to him. She could feel the smooth material of his shirt on her back, the strong chest muscles, the pounding of his heart.

She moved her head slightly to one side and felt his lips brush her cheek, then come to rest at the corner of her mouth, opening slightly and pulling at her upper lip gently with his teeth.

She sighed deeply, bereft by now of any will or desire to stop him, mindlessly responding to his fiery touch. One hand moved slowly now on her throat, across the burning skin of her upper chest, and into the hollow between her breasts. The feathery light touch slid downward, over her ribcage to her abdomen, then back up over her breast, settling there for one heart-stopping moment.

Then his hands bit into her shoulders and he turned her roughly around to face him. Sarah opened her eyes, dazed with passion, and looked up at him. The neatly combed hair was in total disarray, falling over his forehead. She reached up a hand and smoothed it back, the coarse black strands springy under her touch.

His black eyes bored into her. 'I want you, Sarah,' he breathed harshly.

She put her fingers on the finely-etched mouth. 'I know,' she whispered. 'It's all right.'

He gathered her into his arms then and kissed her hungrily, fiercely. She clung to him, responding to his kiss completely, with her whole being. As they clung together, his strong thighs pressed against hers, propelling her backwards into the darkened bedroom. When they reached the side of the bed he tore his mouth from hers and put a hand under her chin, tilting her head up to face his burning eyes.

'Sarah, I told you I wouldn't force

anything from you, and I meant it. I only want what's freely given. Say the word, and I'll take you home right now, before it's too late.'

She smiled and ran her hands down from his shoulders over his chest, then slid them up under the cuffs of his shirt, over the fine silky hair, the taut tendons and muscles.

'The word is yes,' she said.

He clasped her face in his hands then and rubbed his thumbs along her cheekbones and shook his head slowly from side to side.

'What is there about you, Sarah, that makes me feel so . . . so . . .'

His mouth came down on hers gently, playfully. His hands went to the back of her head, his lips parted, and the kiss intensified into a blinding, sensuous exploration of her mouth, on and on until she began to tremble with desire.

At last he pulled away from her. 'I want to see you, Sarah,' he gasped. 'All of you, every lovely inch.'

In one deft movement, he untied the

towelling robe and slipped it down over her arms. He raked her body up and down with his dark eyes, feasting on the sight of her by the shaft of light spilling across them through the open door of the bathroom.

Then, his eyes never leaving her, Sarah watched him as he stripped off his own clothes, revealing his slim, tautly-muscled body in all its masculine beauty. He was exactly as she had imagined him, lithe and strong, his stomach flat, his chest covered with a light mat of dark hair.

He reached out both hands and ran them down her body, from her shoulders to her knees, then back up again to rest on her breasts. Panting now, Sarah arched towards him, her shoulders back, aching with sheer bliss under his touch.

He bent his dark head and, cupping one full breast in his hand, took the taut nipple into his mouth. Sarah groaned aloud as tongues of fire licked through her. She clutched at his hair, drawing him closer to her.

Then he eased her on to the bed, his hands and mouth eagerly exploring her writhing body, and when he covered her and they were united at last, she clung to him in an ecstasy of joy and surrender, possessing him as fully as he did her.

When Sarah awoke, the first faint rays of early morning sunshine shone dimly through the coarse muslin curtains at the bedroom windows. Her back felt as though it were on fire. As she blinked a little in the semi-darkness, memory came flooding back into her mind.

She glanced down. The bedclothes were around her waist, and a large tanned hand was resting lightly on her bare breast. She turned her head on the pillow and saw Sloan lying beside her, half-covered, his face buried in her shoulder.

She smiled and turned slightly towards him to kiss the dark, coarse hair, tousled in sleep. He stirred, and the hand on her breast tightened. Slowly, inch by inch, she eased herself out of bed. She slipped on the towelling robe, lying on the floor where it had been dropped the night before, and stood for a moment looking down at the sleeping man.

Sloan Sheridan. She still couldn't believe it. Last night, just before she had drifted off to sleep in his arms, she had wondered fleetingly how she would feel next morning about what she'd done. Now she knew.

She felt so totally fulfilled she could hardly believe it. Sloan's lovemaking had satisfied her beyond her wildest dreams, made her feel so desirable as a woman that she would never again doubt her own powers of attraction.

Of course she knew it would end, but for now he belonged to her, and that would be enough. Although Sloan never stayed with a woman long—six months had been the limit since she had known him—while the affair lasted he was absolutely faithful. He wasn't a promiscuous man. She would just have to be satisfied with that.

She took up the pile of clothing Sloan had

found for her the night before and went into the bathroom. She let the water flow slowly into the tub so that it wouldn't awaken Sloan. While it ran, she rummaged in the medicine chest for aspirin. There was a full bottle on the top shelf, and as she reached for it her eye fell on a neat row of feminine cosmetics on the bottom shelf.

There were two lipsticks, a small bottle of expensive liquid make-up, mascara, eye-shadow and a jar of cleansing cream. She went rigid at the sight, and then began to wonder why. It came as no surprise to her that Sloan had entertained women in his house, his bed, before her. She had already come to terms with that.

Yet accepting an abstract fact and facing the physical evidence of it were two different things. She shivered a little. Her skin felt suddenly cold and clammy. Taking down the bottle of aspirin, she firmly closed the cabinet door.

I must put such thoughts out of my head, she told herself as she bathed. I went into this with my eyes open. I love Sloan; I want to be with him as long as I can, as long as he wants me.

But wasn't that the problem? she thought as she dried her still sore skin gingerly. She sighed and reached for the pile of clothes. It was loving him so much that made the situation so painful to her.

The clothes Sloan had found were a little large for her, but were well made and obviously expensive. There was a deep cherry red pair of woollen pants and a pale pink knit pullover. A brunette's colours, she thought, surveying herself in the mirror, and once again her blood ran cold.

Whose clothes were they? Leonie's? Ariel Boone's? Any one of a half dozen others she could recall, leaving aside the ones she didn't know about.

She went back into the bedroom. Sloan was still deeply asleep, one arm flung over his head, the other lying at his side. Had she really lain beside him last night in the darkness, really surrendered to him with a mindless ardour that now brought a flush of shame to her cheeks. In the cold light of day, standing there fully dressed in another woman's clothes, the whole episode took on a different perspective.

She wondered how many other women had stood here just as she was now, looking down at the same sleeping man. She thought of Derek and the terrible jealous suspicions that had eaten at her whenever he'd been away from home, working late, on business trips, out with the boys. All lies. Could she go through that again? Wouldn't it be the same thing all over again? But Sloan wasn't Derek. Derek had been her husband, had made vows, promises.

She took up her bag from the dressing-table and slowly walked down the curving staircase to the wide hallway below looking for the kitchen. A cup of coffee was what she needed. The aspirin hadn't taken effect yet, and her back smarted painfully. She'd feel better when she'd had some breakfast.

On her search for the kitchen she

wandered through the rooms on the main floor, all immaculate, all stark, severe and Sloan-like. There was a spacious living room with a fireplace, a formal dining room, and finally a smaller, more cluttered room that was obviously Sloan's study.

A large desk was by the window, with neat stacks of paper strewn on top. Bookshelves lined the walls, and a massive globe was in one corner. There were a few photographs on the desk, and as she walked over to it she could see that one was of his father, the other of his sister.

She turned to go when a small card with Sloan's slashing black handwriting on it caught her eye on the surface of the desk. She glanced down at it, drawn irresistibly by its familiarity.

'Fond memories, no regrets,' she read. She stood quite still, staring down at it for a long time. There was no salutation, no date. Perhaps he had prepared it in advance for her, she thought wildly, since she wouldn't be there to do it for him. Or was he even now involved with another woman she knew nothing about?

She shrank inside herself, seemed to shrivel and die. The cosmetics in the bathroom, the clothes she was wearing, and now this. She couldn't bear it. She stood there for a long time, thinking, then at last she knew what she had to do.

She took out the pad and pencil from her bag and sat down at the desk.

'Sloan,' she wrote, 'I've gone home, and I won't be coming back to work for you. Please don't call me or try to contact me in any way. I see now it just won't work.'

There was no need to say anything more, she decided as she read it over, but before she signed her name, on an impulse, she added the words, 'Fond memories, no regrets.'

She ripped the page out of her notebook and set it down on the desk near the card Sloan had written. Then she went quietly out of the front door and started walking down the steep hill. Eventually she found a telephone booth and called a taxi. When it came, she got inside and gave the driver her address in Berkeley. She leaned her head back on the seat and numbly gave herself up to her misery.

Sarah wasn't surprised when Sloan made no effort to contact her in the days that followed. With the Alvarez trial coming up in a week, he would be wholly taken up with last-minute preparations. Besides that, she was all too familiar with his lighthearted attitude towards his romantic adventures. She was certain he would just chalk her up as a dubious victory. He'd got what he wanted from her—surrender. It probably wouldn't bother him that she had been the one to end the affair, almost before it had begun.

During the week after her flight from Sloan's house that Sunday morning, however, she visualised many times in her imagination the look on his face when he found her note on his desk. How had he taken it? With a philosophical smile? Outraged fury? Satisfaction that she had eliminated herself before he tired of her? She had no way of knowing.

In spite of her thorough knowledge of the way his mind worked through their long professional association, there was much about Sloan Sheridan that was a mystery to her. He hid a great deal behind that cool mask of his.

On Wednesday, her mother called her late in the afternoon.

'Come to dinner tonight, Sarah,' she said. 'We have some exciting news.'

Sarah needed some exciting news just about then. She had moped around the house for three days, unable to get Sloan off her mind or think about her future. No matter how hard she tried, she couldn't erase him from her thoughts. His kisses still burned on her lips, his touch on her body, and the image of him bending over her, brown eyes alight with passion, haunted her dreams as well as her waking hours.

Every time the telephone rang, her heart would quicken, wondering if it might be Sloan calling. It never was, and although she longed to hear his voice, she knew it was better for her in the end that he leave her alone. She still had grave doubts about her power to resist him, no matter how many resolutions she made.

Her parents greeted her that evening with beaming faces. She could tell that her father was struggling hard to remain cool and composed, but her mother felt no such compunction, and immediately burst out with the news.

'Darling, the Bar Association is going to hold a special dinner honouring your father next month. "For thirty years of dedicated service to upholding and nurturing the highest standards of the legal profession in the San Francisco Bay Area," ' she quoted from the engraved invitation she held in her hand. She thrust it at Sarah.

'Oh, Dad,' Sarah cried when she had read it, 'I'm so proud of you!' She threw her arms around him and kissed him warmly.

'The fuss you women make,' he said grumpily. 'This is probably their way of gently telling me I'm over the hill and easing me out of my job before senility sets in.'

'You're probably right,' said Sarah, falling in with his mood. 'You might get a gold watch out of it, anyway,' she added casually.

'More likely a bronze plaque,' he rejoined with a smile.

'You could put it up by your shaving mirror to remind you every morning how important you are.'

He threw back his head and laughed. They were much alike and understood each other perfectly. But Sarah's mother stood and glared at them both.

'You two! Sarah, you shouldn't encourage him. It's a great honour, and your father richly deserves it.' Then she smiled. 'Wait until Margaret gets here—*she* knows how to enter into the spirit of a celebration!'

Over dinner they discussed the great event. It was set for the middle of August, three weeks away, and would be held at the Claremont, an elderly but still imposing hotel high in the Berkeley hills not far from the campus. It was to be a gala, black-tie affair, with all the Bay Area legal luminaries in attendance.

As Sarah drove home that night, she wondered if Sloan would be there. If the Alvarez trial was over by then, he certainly would attend. All her father's old students would want to be there to honour him. How would she react when she saw him? How would he?

She sighed as she put the car in the garage and went into the house. She'd just have to cross that bridge when she came to it.

On the following Monday, the Alvarez case came to trial. The newspapers were full of it, and Sarah eagerly followed its progress day by day. The reports were contradictory, some commentators trying and sentencing the doctor even before the jury was selected, while others confided to their readers that with Sloan Sheridan defending him, Jack the Ripper would have gone free.

On Wednesday, Warren Langley called her.

'Sorry to butt in on your vacation, Sarah,' came his distraught voice, 'but I've misplaced Mrs Layton's deposition transcript. Do you have any bright ideas where it might be?'

So Sloan hadn't told him she had left for good, she thought. What did that mean? Probably only that he'd been so busy he'd overlooked the fact himself. Or forgotten it.

She thought a moment, wrenching her mind back to the office details she had deliberately put out of her mind.

'I keep all deposition transcripts of current cases in the bottom drawer of the large filing cabinet behind my desk. It's plainly marked.'

'I looked there,' Warren went on in a plaintive tone. 'I know I had it—I just can't find it.' He groaned. 'Sloan will flay me alive when he finds out!'

Sarah's mind raced. 'Listen, Warren, don't panic. It was only a copy. All originals have to be filed with the Clerk of Court before trial. I filed Mrs Layton's myself after she signed it. Go down to the Courthouse and get them to make you a copy. It'll cost an arm and a leg, and Sloan may take it out of your hide when he gets the bill, but it's your best bet.'

Warren sighed with deep relief. 'God, thanks a million, Sarah. I was about ready to jump off the Golden Gate bridge! I'll be glad when you get back. Ginny tries hard, but she doesn't have your memory and knack for organisation.'

'She'll learn,' Sarah said quickly. 'Give her time.' She hesitated. 'How's it going? The trial?'

Warren lowered his voice confidentially. 'Not so hot up to now, but tomorrow we're dropping a bombshell. No one knows, not even Ginny, so don't breathe a word.' He paused for dramatic effect. 'Jack Layton's going to take the witness stand after all.'

'Oh, Warren, that's wonderful! Now you won't have to use the pictures. I'm so glad!'

'What pictures?' His voice was bewildered.

'Why, the pictures Sloan and I took of Martha Layton and her mother at their house in Sausalito. Remember, you had to stay in Santa Barbara with Jack Layton, so Sloan asked me to go with him.'

'I'm sorry, Sarah, but I haven't a clue what you're talking about.'

Sarah didn't know what to think. Had Warren forgotten? He was in a terrible state over the trial and the lost deposition. Or had Sloan lied to her? Did it really make any differences now?

'How is he?' she asked at last. 'Sloan?'

'Oh, you know Sloan. He's always the same. The great stone face, barking orders right and left. Impatient, demanding. But, boy, is he something to watch in a courtroom! I've never seen anything like it.

He seems a little more tired and distracted than usual, but that's probably from the pressure of the trial.'

'Most likely,' she agreed.

'Listen, Sarah, I've got to run. Thanks a million for the tip about the Layton dep. I should have known that myself.'

Sarah slowly hung up the phone. *Had* Sloan lied to her about the reason for their trip to Sausalito? If so, why? Surely he wouldn't have gone to such lengths just to get her alone, not the week before an important trial.

She sighed. The man was an enigma. There was no telling what went through his mind. She was glad at any rate that he wouldn't have to use those photographs at the trial. They had left a bad taste in her mouth.

She was glad, too, that Jack Layton was well enough to testify. That would indeed rock the other side, and pretty well clinch Sloan's case. Another victory for the great Sloan Sheridan, she thought wryly. Was there no end to his cleverness, his ability to get what he wanted?

Well, he didn't get me, she thought as she went into the kitchen to fix her evening meal. Even though she had surrendered so mindlessly to him once, she had had the sense not to blunder into a full-blown affair with him. She wondered how many other women had walked out on him first, and congratulated herself on her narrow escape.

The next morning, on an impulse, Sarah took the train into the City to watch the Alvarez trial. She wanted to be there when Sloan produced his star witness.

Judge Becker's courtroom was crowded, but Sarah knew one of the bailiffs from Sloan's previous trials, and he found her a seat at the back. It was eleven o'clock, and they had just resumed the proceedings after the morning recess.

Sarah glanced around. The twelve jurors, solemn-faced with their heavy re-sponsibilities, sat in the jury box over to one side facing the spectators. Judge Becker, impressive in his long black robes, sat behind the bench, wooden gavel in hand. There was the District Attorney himself, with two young assistants, at a front table facing the judge.

She saw Warren, at the defendant's table with Dr Alvarez, but there wasn't a sign of Sloan. She heard the judge ask for the next witness, saw Warren approach the bench to speak to him. Then the double doors at the back of the courtroom opened and Sloan appeared, pushing Jack Layton ahead of him in a wheelchair.

The whole courtroom gasped in unison. Judge Becker banged his gavel, the bailiff was shouting, 'Order! Order in the court!' and soon the babble of voices quieted down so that Jack Layton could be sworn in.

For the next hour, Sarah sat entranced as Sloan worked his magic. He seemed to tower over every other person there. He was dressed in a lightweight grey suit, and whether he moved around or stood stock still, the ease and grace and authority of his manner dominated the crowded courtroom.

She was impressed, deeply impressed, even though she knew his tactics so well. It was one thing to know what should be done, quite another actually to carry it off. When he finished, just before noon, Sarah could tell that the jurors were similarly impressed.

The judge banged his gavel announcing the noon recess. Sarah waited impatiently for the people ahead of her on the wooden bench to get moving. She didn't want Sloan to see her. She had planned to leave early to avoid an encounter with him, but had been so mesmerised by his performance she had lost all track of time.

She glanced his way and saw his eyes sweep the courtroom. Quickly she turned her head so he wouldn't recognise her. She was in the very back row and didn't think he would notice her in the crowd of people standing there waiting to get out.

At last she was at the aisle. Before she left, she couldn't resist one backward glance. She saw him about halfway up the aisle, bending over a woman sitting on the end, a brilliant smile lighting his stern features, one hand on the woman's arm.

Sarah couldn't see her face, only the back of her head. Through the crowd of people still milling about, she noticed only that the woman was a brunette. She stumbled out of the courtroom and out into the street, blinded by the tears that stung her eyes.

CHAPTER NINE

ON the night of the Bar Association dinner honouring her father, Sarah sat in her living room waiting for her parents to pick her up. It had been three weeks since the Alvarez trial. The doctor had been acquitted, as she expected.

She had heard nothing from Sloan. Warren Langley had called her on the day she was due back from her two-week vacation, and was appalled when she told him she wouldn't be returning. Apparently Sloan hadn't mentioned it to him.

She went to the front window to watch for her father's car. Margaret and Robert would be with them, up from Santa Barbara for the occasion. It seemed they were finally getting their problems worked out. She would be a fifth wheel tonight, and half regretted that she hadn't asked Warren to accompany her. She pulled aside the curtain to see the street better, and thought about that telephone conversation with him.

He had told her that Sloan had gone on some kind of vacation trip right after the trial, destination unknown. He had seemed exhausted, Warren said, drained of energy after the gruelling trial and months of concentrated preparation.

That didn't sound like Sloan, she thought now. He usually bounced right back from his trials, eager to get on to the next challenge. She wondered if he had gone alone on his trip or had taken the brunette she'd seen in the courtroom that day.

Her family arrived just then, and she hurried out of the house and down the path to the car. Her one thought as she greeted them and climbed into the front seat next to her mother was that if Sloan was gone on an extended trip, at least she wouldn't have to face him tonight.

*   *   *

The Claremont Hotel was a large, sprawling structure built on the side of a hill in a setting of large evergreens and well-tended gardens. It had been the scene of hundreds of important functions for as long as Sarah could remember, everything from debutante balls to receptions for visiting dignitaries and government officials.

For this evening's celebration, the large central dining room had been pre-empted. There was one long head table just beneath the bandstand for the honoured guests, with a great many smaller round tables placed around the polished dance floor. The white damask tablecloths gleamed, and black-clad waiters hovered discreetly in the background.

Sarah sat at the head table between Margaret and Robert, surveying the gathering crowd. She had dressed carefully that evening in a long white silk crêpe dress that showed off her tan. It had a deeply cut halter neckline that had dismayed her when she first put it on, but in experimenting with it, she discovered that if she was careful not to make any sudden movements, the bare breasts underneath were not even remotely visible.

She had made up her face carefully and discreetly, with a soft pinky-beige lipstick, a light blusher and just a touch of dark mascara on her long, thick eyelashes. Her golden hair hung loose, heavy and gleaming, to her shoulders, where it curved slightly outward.

As she sat there, through the dinner and the speeches afterwards, her eyes swept the room casually several times, but there was no sign of Sloan. She was half relieved, half disappointed, but hadn't really expected to see him. She did, however, see Warren Langley's fair head, and knew she would have some awkward explaining to do about her presence here if they ran into each other later.

Finally, after-dinner drinks were served, the band started playing sedate, old-fashioned dance tunes, and couples began to drift out on to the polished floor. Sarah danced once with Robert and once with the president of the Bar Association, and was now dancing with her father.

'Well, Dad,' she said, smiling up at him as they moved slowly around the crowded dance floor, 'are you feeling properly impressed with yourself after all those flattering speeches?'

His hazel eyes, so much like her own, twinkled down on her. 'Oh, my, yes, Sadie. I may never be able to get a hat on again, my head is so swelled out of proportion!'

The speeches had been highly complimentary, recounting in detail Dean Tennant's many years of devoted service at the University and in legal organisations throughout the Bay area. There had been several testimonials from his former students, one a United States Senator, two of them judges, all of them prominent in the legal profession.

The music stopped. As they started back to the head table, Warren Langley came walking towards them. He was alone. There would be no avoiding him, Sarah thought, then wondered why she should even want to. It made no difference now if he found out she was the Dean's daughter. His eyes goggled at her appreciatively as he took in the clinging dress, the shining hair.

'Sarah,' he choked out, 'you look ... I mean, I hardly recognised you!'

She laughed. 'Hello, Warren. I'd like you to meet my father, John Tennant. Dad, this is Warren Langley, one of the lawyers at the Sheridan firm.'

Warren gazed up at the tall, dignified man beside her in awestruck confusion. His eyes darted to Sarah, still grinning at him, then back to her father. Finally, he recovered himself and stuck out a hand.

'Sir,' he croaked as they shook hands, 'it's an honour to meet you. I never thought ... I mean, I didn't know ... Sarah never said ...'

Dean Tennant laughed. 'I'm afraid my daughter doesn't like to acknowledge her parentage. I think she's ashamed of me!'

John Tennant's warm, friendly manner put the young man at ease so that Warren was able to join in the joke, too, and the three of them stood laughing easily together. Then she saw him. The laughter died on Sarah's lips and her hand tightened on her father's arm.

Sloan Sheridan was walking their way. He was taller than most of the men and dazzling in his well-cut formal black suit. He moved towards them with a lithe grace, slowly, unhurriedly, one hand in his jacket pocket, and as she watched him, transfixed, Sarah felt suddenly as though they were the only two people in the room.

There was a humming noise in her head, blotting out the sounds around her. Her hands felt damp and clammy. Her heart fluttered wildly, and for one terrible moment, she was actually afraid she might lose her balance and fall.

'Sloan,' she heard her father say through the thick wool in her head. 'Sloan Sheridan! I didn't think you were here.'

'I just got back today, John,' came Sloan's easy voice. 'I've been out of town.'

The two men shook hands warmly, like the old friends they were, and gradually Sarah's head began to clear. The close presence of her father steadied her. She loosened her grip on his arm.

'I believe you know my daughter, Sarah,' her father was saying in a joking tone. 'Come out of the closet at last!' He laughed. 'I guess she decided she'd either have to admit to me as her parent before the world or stay home tonight and miss the festivities.'

For one brief moment, Sloan's heavy eyebrows lifted in surprise. Then he nodded briefly at her. His expression was grave, but Sarah recognised the latent anger in the black eyes.

'Yes, of course,' he said easily. 'I know Sarah—your *daughter*—quite well.' Sarah blushed as she recalled just how well he knew her. The music started up again. 'Would you care to dance?' he asked her.

She couldn't refuse, especially when her father, beaming paternally, drew aside and began to walk off with an ecstatic Warren.

Sloan held her lightly, almost at a distance, for some time. Sarah stared miserably over his shoulder, waiting for the axe to fall. Finally he drew back and glared down at her.

'You've got a lot of explaining to do,' he ground out.

Sarah knew instinctively from his tone, the tautness of his shoulder muscles under her hand, the way he gripped her, that he was extremely angry. She stumbled a little and his hand on her waist tightened.

Then, suddenly, she asked herself why she was so frightened of him. They were surrounded by a roomful of people. He was no longer her boss. And what gave him the right to demand explanations from her, anyway?

She gave him a cool look. 'I don't see that I have to explain myself to you in any way, but if you're talking about my father, there's no mystery. I just didn't want to be accused of using his influence in my job.'

'I was not referring to your father,' he said clearly, 'although it beats me how a fine man like John Tennant could have produced such a deceitful, ungrateful daughter.'

She glared up at him, her mouth open. 'Deceitful! Ungrateful! How dare you? And what about you? It seems to me you have a lot to answer for yourself before you go around demanding explanations from me!'

Their eyes were locked together now, both breathing hard in their mutual anger. They had broken apart and stood glaring at each other in the middle of the floor.

'Such as?' he said at last.

Sarah made an impatient gesture, her breast heaving. 'Such as,' she accused, 'cosmetics in the medicine chest, a woman's wardrobe tucked away in your house, one of your nasty farewell notes on your desk, a new brunette in the courtroom at the Alvarez trial, and,' she spluttered on, 'an outright lie about that dreadful trip to Sausalito!'

She stood before him, her hands clenched at her sides, uncaring about the interested glances they were receiving from the other couples and all caution about the insecure halter top of the white dress abandoned.

Sloan's eyes were widened now in amazement at her explosive tirade. No one talked to Sloan Sheridan like that, she thought, and was doubly glad she had. She met his dark gaze head on, her chin lifted.

'That's quite a catalogue,' he said finally in a bemused tone.

Then she watched in growing uneasiness as the dark eyes travelled downward and a slow, wicked smile curled on the thin lips. Hating herself for caring what he thought, she glanced down at the bodice of her dress, gaping partly open now, to reveal quite clearly to any interested eye that she wore nothing underneath.

Sloan grabbed her by the hand. 'Come on,' he growled. 'We're getting out of here.'

He pulled her roughly along. 'I'm tired of entertaining all these people gawking at us, and we're going to get a few things straightened out once and for all.'

Stumbling and protesting, clutching the bodice of her dress, Sarah had no choice but to follow him. She knew he was quite capable of making a scene, and she didn't want to embarrass her parents.

Outside the hotel, the evening was still warm and balmy from the heat of the day. There were several paths meandering through the gardens, well lit along the way, and Sloan strode down one of these now, pulling her along behind him.

They came to a wooden bench beside a fountain near a large bed of roses, the sweet scent heavy on the still air. Sloan took her by the shoulders and sat her down hard on the bench. He stood before her, long legs apart, knuckles on his lean hips.

'Now,' he said in an authoritative tone, 'you listen to me. The female paraphernalia you saw in my house belongs to my sister.

Occasionally I can coax her up to San Francisco to stay with me for a few days, and I try to make her feel as much at home as possible so she won't panic.'

He paused, waiting, looking down at her, but she could neither speak nor look at him. She hung her head. Why was he doing this? Why couldn't he just leave her alone?

'The mysterious brunette in the courtroom was also Kathleen, although God knows why I'm bothering to explain all this to you.' She glanced up at him then. He ran a hand distractedly through his thick coarse hair. 'You walked out on me, after all.' His eyes brooded at her. 'Why, Sarah? Why did you leave that morning? I thought . . . Hell, I don't know what I thought!'

He sat down beside her on the bench and took both her hands in his. 'The night we had together was so perfect,' he went on in a low voice. 'I'd never known anything like it. You responded to me as though . . . as though . . .' His voice broke off.

Sarah gave him a quick glance. Sloan

Sheridan at a loss for words? She could hardly believe it! He sat now turning her small hands over in his large ones. His shoulders slumped forward, his elbows resting on his knees. In spite of herself, Sarah's heart went out to him.

'Sloan,' she murmured. He looked at her, and she shrugged her shoulders. 'What can I say? How can I make you understand?' She took a deep breath. 'I told you once I wasn't your type. What I meant by that was that I could never tolerate a brief affair. Much as I respond to you, much as I love being with you, you must believe me when I tell you that a relationship without commitment would utterly destroy me.' She shuddered. 'I had that with Derek—I don't ever want it again.'

'Damn it,' he ground out, 'I'm not Derek!' He took her roughly by the shoulders and turned her around to face him. 'Just give it a chance, Sarah.' He shook her a little. 'You're so lovely, and I want you so much.'

He kissed her lightly, her hair, her forehead, her eyelids, the tip of her nose. He put his cheek next to hers, and she drew in her breath at the familiar scent of him, the gentle rasping of his jaw on her smooth skin, his breath at her ear.

'You want me, too,' he murmured in her ear. 'You know you do.' His arms came around her now, his hands moving slowly over her bare back, and she gasped as his long fingers slipped under the loose edges of the halter top to run tantalisingly along the fullness of her breasts.

Only the thought of her family, inside the hotel, wondering probably where she had gone, stopped her from melting into his arms and agreeing to anything he asked of her.

She put her hands on his chest, pushed him away gently, and drew back from him.

'Oh, yes, Sloan, I want you,' she admitted, and longed to tell him just how desperately she loved him. 'But it's not enough.' She rose to her feet. 'I've got to go now. My family will be looking for me.'

He gave her one long look, then got to his feet. They walked back down the path to the hotel. Sloan left her abruptly at the main entrance where the long drive curved around in front.

'Goodnight, Sarah,' he said in a distant tone. 'Please give your father my con-gratulations again.' He turned then and strode down the driveway. Sarah watched after him until he was lost from view, then with a heavy heart, slowly went inside to find her family.

During the next few days, Sarah thought about that conversation with Sloan in the garden constantly. She turned it over and over again in her mind, examining it from all angles, until she thought she would go mad. Why had he bothered to make all those explanations? Just to get her in bed again? She'd never known him to go to such trouble over a woman before. Usually they did the pursuing, while all he did was cock an eyebrow, or smile in a certain way, and they fell at his feet.

She still wasn't certain she had done the right thing in rejecting him. She knew that she ached for him, wanted him, loved him, and half a dozen times she had found her hand on the telephone to call him. However, there was still too much not explained to suit her.

What about the card she'd found? Had Sloan been involved all along with a woman she knew nothing about? And that suspicious trip to the Laytons'. Had he tricked her into going, lied to her about needing those photographs? Warren had known nothing about it.

Her little nephew, Billy, had been staying with her for a few days while Margaret and Robert went off on a reconciliation trip to Lake Tahoe. They were due back some time today, and watching the little boy now, as he played happily with his toy trucks out on her back lawn, Sarah realised how sorry she would be to give him up.

He was, indeed, a docile little boy, with a sunny disposition and the ability to amuse himself without whining for attention. One of those lucky children, she thought, who seemed to be born feeling at home in the world.

It was one of those dry hot days in late August where the very air seemed parched. Sarah had set the sprinkler on the thirsty lawn near where Billy was playing. She was dressed in shorts and a strapless knit top, the coolest clothes she owned, lounging on the small brick patio in the shade, watching the little boy as he banged his wooden trucks together in murderous collisions.

His play took him closer and closer to the sprinkler, and in a flash, before Sarah could stop him, he jumped into it and was running up and down through the cool spray, his trucks forgotten, screaming with glee.

Sarah leaped up and ran to him. She wasn't sure his careful mother would approve. She grabbed for him as he ran out of the water, but his wet body, dressed only in little knit shorts, was slippery, and she fell forward, right into the spray.

She gasped as the cold water hit her hot skin, but Billy tugged at her, shrieking, and soon they were chasing each other through the sprinkler, laughing and splashing.

'All right, young man,' she cried at last, swooping the squirming child up into her arms, 'your mother will be here soon, and she'll skin me if she sees you like this!'

It wasn't until she started towards the house that she saw him, half hidden in the shade of the patio roof, leaning up against the house.

'Sloan!' she choked out. 'How long have you been standing there?'

He began walking towards her. Billy, sensing his opportunity, wriggled out of her arms and ran back to the inviting sprinkler. Sarah could only stare at the tall man moving towards her. He was dressed in dark trousers and a light cotton shirt, the sleeves rolled up above his elbows. All she could think of was how handsome he looked, and how glad she was to see him.

'We have some unfinished business to attend to,' he announced calmly. He stood towering over her, looking her over carefully from head to toe, a malicious glint in the dark eyes.

She was suddenly conscious of how she must look, the soaked knit top clinging to her body that hid nothing of her slim, firm figure, the hair plastered wetly to her head. She bit her lower lip and hugged her arms across her clearly defined breasts.

'I said everything I had to say that night,' she muttered in a low, accusing voice. 'You have no right . . .'

'I have every right, damn it!' he shouted. Then, in a gentler tone, he said, 'I've brought you a present.'

He walked back to the shade of the patio, stooped over to pick up a long box, then came back and thrust it at her. Just at that moment Margaret appeared through the back gate.

'Sarah,' she called, 'we're back!' She caught sight of Sloan, then, and stopped short. 'Oh—er——' she faltered, 'excuse me.' She looked around nervously. 'Where's Billy?'

Then she saw her son sitting joyfully on the sprinkler head, water spurting over him, and ran to him. Sarah steeled herself for the fireworks and ran into the house to get a towel, setting the box Sloan had given her on the dresser in her bedroom on her way.

When she came back, she saw that Sloan, grinning broadly, had retrieved the drenched child, while Margaret hovered anxiously at his side.

Sarah ran over to them and wrapped the towel around the loudly protesting little boy. Margaret drew him out of Sloan's arms, scolding and clucking disapprovingly. When she had reassured herself that Billy was quite all right, she raised her eyes and looked first at Sarah, then at Sloan, a long appraising look.

'Well, Sarah,' she said at last, 'thanks for

taking care of Billy for me. We had a super time. Robert's waiting for me in the car. I— er—I'd better be going now. I'll call you later.'

'Goodbye, Margaret,' Sloan said politely, turning to her. 'It was nice to see you again. Remember me to Robert.'

Sarah was jolted out of her trance. 'Oh, Margaret, don't forget Billy's things.'

'I'll get them later,' Margaret said quickly, and scurried off.

When she was gone, Sarah found she couldn't look at Sloan. What was he doing here? She felt like a drowned rat, her hair hanging damply around her shoulders, her virtually transparent clothes clinging to her.

She jumped when he made an abrupt gesture with his hands. 'For God's sake, Sarah, go get some clothes on or I won't answer for what happens!'

She opened her mouth, then saw the look on his face, and ducked quickly past him. She ran into her bedroom and shut the door, leaning back against it, her knees weak, her heart thudding painfully. Then she stripped off her sodden garments, dried herself briskly, and put on clean underwear and a short candy-striped cotton shift.

After she had blown her hair dry, she paused at the bedroom door. Would he still be there? And what in the world would she say to him if he was? Then her eye fell on the box she had set on the dresser, forgotten in all the confusion of Margaret's arrival.

She walked over to the dresser, opened the box and pushed aside the layers of crisp green tissue paper. There, nestled inside, were at least two dozen pristine, palely gleaming white roses.

'White roses! What did that mean? There was a card. With trembling fingers she reached down, picked it up, opened it. In Sloan's slashing black handwriting, the message said, 'To a long and happy future.'

She didn't understand. Was this his way of saying goodbye, wishing her well as she departed from his employ? She had to find out. She gathered up the box and went into the kitchen to put the roses in water. Sloan was standing there leaning up against the sink, his back to her, arms braced on the counter, staring out of the window.

'Thank you for the roses, Sloan,' she said carefully. 'They're beautiful.'

He turned slowly around and watched her as she fumbled in a cabinet for a vase, then put the roses inside it.

'Is that all you have to say?' he asked finally as she came to the sink. She brushed past him to run water into the vase.

She gave him a quick upward glance. They were not quite touching, but her skin prickled in acute awareness of his close proximity.

'I . . .' She hesitated. 'What more is there to say?' she asked limply.

His eyes bored into her. 'How about, "I love you, Sloan. I want to marry you." '

The room started to spin. Had she heard right? He couldn't possibly be serious. Very carefully, she set down the vase and shut off the tap, her eyes cast down.

'Don't joke about a thing like that, Sloan.' She felt hot tears sting her eyes. How could he be so cruel?

Slowly he turned her around to face him. He reached out and with his thumbs wiped away the tears that glistened on her cheeks. There was a look of gentleness in his face she had seen only once before, with his sister.

'It's true, isn't it?' he asked. 'Is it so hard for you to say? I'll go first, if you like. I love you, Sarah. I want to marry you.'

'You're serious,' she said at last.

'Of course I'm serious. Have you ever known me to say something I didn't mean?'

He gathered her into his arms, then, and held her carefully, protectively, like a piece of fine china he was afraid might break.

'My darling girl,' he murmured in her ear, rocking her gently, 'I fell hopelessly, irrevocably in love with you from the minute it penetrated my thick skull that you weren't married. From then on I was lost.'

'But you knew all along I wasn't married,'

she protested. Was this really happening? She must be dreaming.

'I guess I did. I just didn't want to acknowledge it.' He gazed down at her. 'You cast quite a potent spell, Sarah, even in that touch-me-not disguise of yours. You terrified me. That icy reserve, that cool efficient manner. Everything about you warned "Hands off." ' He grinned crookedly. 'How can a mere man resist that kind of challenge?'

Sarah's heart was singing. Sloan loves me. Sloan wants to marry me. She reached up a hand and put it lightly on his cheek. 'Then you did trick me into that trip to the Laytons' to get those photographs!'

He shrugged. 'Not really. Call it a tactical manoeuvre. I did think I might be able to use some damaging photographs of the Layton women if Jack Layton didn't live, but I'll have to admit the brilliant inspiration first came to me when Warren was conveniently unavailable to help me.' He took the hand still resting on his cheek and kissed the palm. 'It wasn't really a deception,' he murmured against it. 'Are you angry?'

How could she be, she thought, when his main objective had been to be alone with her? She smiled and shook her head. 'No, I'm not angry.' Then she paused, sobering. Could a man like Sloan ever be able to settle for one woman? Much as she loved him, she couldn't bear a repetition of Derek's idea of marriage.

'Tell me,' she asked lightly, 'do you think you'll be able to give up all those dashing brunettes?'

He put his palms flat on either side of her face and looked down deeply into her eyes. 'Darling, I'm thirty-six years old. Since I was eighteen, for half my life, women have only been a diversion for me. My work always came first.' He kissed her hungrily. 'Then you came along, and I saw how empty it all was without real love, without commitment. Without you.'

She reached up, then, and twined her

arms around his neck. He gathered her roughly to him, pressing her all along the hard length of his body, and she strained against him as his strong hands travelled down from her shoulders to her hips.

She leaned her head back and looked up at him. 'Sloan,' she said.

'Mmm?' His eyes were half closed. He was unbuttoning her shift now, pushing aside the thin material, his hands roaming possessively over her breasts. It was unmistakably apparent how aroused he was, but there was one more thing that still troubled her, and she had to know.

'What about the card, Sloan?'

'What card?' He bent down and nuzzled at her breast, bare now under his burning lips.

She put her hands on his skull, the thick dark hair springing in her fingers, and forced his head up. He looked at her with passion-dazed eyes.

'The card on your desk. Remember? "Fond memories, no regrets."'

'Oh, that card,' he said absently. 'I was cleaning out my desk and came across it.' He chuckled. 'I used to keep a supply of them until you came along and took over the job for me.'

His lips came down hungrily on hers, and she met his consuming kiss eagerly, the last shred of doubt gone. The shift dropped to the floor, and when he picked her up in his arms to carry her into the bedroom, her eyes fell on the vase of roses still sitting on the counter. White roses, she thought happily to herself, and remembered the card.

'To a long and happy future.' Somehow she knew that with Sloan, that was exactly what it would be.

THE END

THESE ARE THE OTHER TITLES
TO LOOK OUT FOR
THIS MONTH

THE SILVER FLAME
by Margaret Pargeter

After surviving an air crash, Jane was told she had been married to Colin Denyer who had lost his life in the crash — and as she had lost her memory she couldn't contradict Colin's disagreeable brother Paul. But what right had Paul to tell her, 'Don't imagine I'd be willing to step into Colin's shoes!' What made him think she wanted him to?

RIDE THE WIND
by Yvonne Whittal

When Steve Beaumont described Loren as a 'walking disaster', it was with reason, because every time she went near him something went badly wrong! But it would be even more of a disaster if she allowed herself to become involved with him — because no woman lasted more than five minutes with Steve Beaumont . . .

EACH MONTH MILLS & BOON PUBLISH
THREE LARGE PRINT ROMANCES
FOR YOU TO LOOK OUT FOR,
AND ENJOY. THESE ARE THE TITLES
FOR NEXT MONTH

———————— * ————————

MATCHMAKER NURSE
by Betty Beaty

YESTERDAY'S SHADOW
by Helen Bianchin

HEAVEN HERE ON EARTH
by Carole Mortimer